64+

64+

Your Ultimate Guide to Medicare & Retirement Planning

Chase Gruening

Published by Game Changer Publishing

Paperback ISBN: 978-1-967424-04-7

Hardcover ISBN: 978-1-967424-05-4

Digital ISBN: 978-1-967424-06-1

www.GameChangerPublishing.com

I would like to dedicate this book to my mother, Tamara Bivins, for always supporting me in everything I have ever done.

READY TO LEARN MORE ABOUT MEDICARE?

Thanks for reading *64+*!
Join our free Medicare 101 webinar—a quick and easy way to get the
information you need,
all in one place.
Scan the QR code to sign up.
It's a simple next step toward feeling confident about Medicare.

Scan the QR Code Here:

64+

YOUR ULTIMATE GUIDE TO MEDICARE & RETIREMENT PLANNING

CHASE GRUENING

GAME CHANGER PUBLISHING

CONTENTS

INTRODUCTION

At my core, I'm a coach. And what I know is teaching people, developing people, and leading people through tough times. My name is Chase Gruening. In my past life, I coached college and high school football for almost a decade. Football has always been a huge part of my life, and coaching has always been a big part of my life, too. But honestly, that portion of my life was unpredictable, and did not pay the bills.

I always tell people I went to college to play football. When you finish playing after four years and earn a degree, people often ask, "What do you want to do?" You don't always have a clear answer. All I really knew was football.

I leaned into that. I went and coached football. And after five years of coaching at the college level, it was really tough on me.

I moved across the country six times in five years. The quality of life was low—I wasn't making much money, the hours were long, and family couldn't be much of a priority.

I knew that wasn't where I wanted to be in the long term. I quickly transitioned to volunteering as a high school football coach for another five years and then got into Medicare and the retirement planning industry. That shift really filled the gap of being able to coach and lead, as I now lead a team of insurance agents and consumers across the country. I'm still teaching and training, but now on a very important topic: Medicare and retirement planning. I'm still teaching, training, leading, and developing, just in a different field.

Why Did I Write This Book?

We provide education in many different ways—online content, weekly Medicare webinars, and in-person seminars. But I know people like to learn in different formats, and reading is one of them. I wanted to check that box by writing a book and delivering the same great education we already offer in other ways.

I hope you see this book as another component of the comprehensive educational content we provide, whether you're reading it in paperback or digital format. This book is for anyone entering Medicare and retirement planning. At Gruening Health and Wealth, Medicare and retirement planning is what we do. We help Medicare beneficiaries and retirees across the country, and this book is designed for those stepping into that stage of life. Think of it as your comprehensive guide to Medicare and retirement planning.

Why Should You Listen to Me?

I've been doing this for nearly a decade. I could list awards and accomplishments, but I believe the best endorsements come from others. We have hundreds of five-star reviews across the internet, and you'll find reviews and testimonials in this book as well. Don't just take my word for it—take theirs.

Thousands of people have worked with us and given us five-star reviews. We're also proud to support our local communities. We have brick-and-mortar locations throughout the country, including downtown Nashville, Dickson, Tennessee, and Springfield, Illinois.

We're licensed in all 50 states and provide educational content nationwide. We're also Better Business Bureau A+ accredited and committed to delivering top-tier service to our clients.

What Will You Get From This Book?

My goal is for you to be fully prepared—*armed and dangerous,* as I like to say—when it comes to Medicare and retirement planning.

I want you to have all the information you need to make the right decision, and we would love to work with you. Ultimately, the goal of this book is to equip you with the knowledge you need to make educated and informed decisions and take action.

First and foremost, thank you for deciding to read this book. We are going to jump right in and guide you through the ins and outs of Medicare and retirement planning.

CHAPTER 1
ORIGINAL MEDICARE

I want to start by talking about my family and how we've helped them. I think back to my first few meetings with my wife's parents —my in-laws.

At the time, they were my future in-laws, and I was with my future wife in Lake Tahoe. My future in-laws were turning 65 and getting ready to go on Medicare.

Obviously, I was excited to have new clients, but when you're working with your in-laws and your family, you really go the extra mile. I learned very quickly from this experience that it's important to treat everyone like family. And the concerns they had were the same concerns as everyone else.

A holistic and individualized approach is what truly matters. You'll see from this story that they had completely different needs. I think back to that hotel room in Lake Tahoe, where we sat down to talk about Medicare.

Just like with any other clients I meet, we started with the foundational process. One of the first things I always ask people is, "What is important to you? What are the questions you want to get checked off your list?" And it's always interesting with married couples because they often have completely different answers. In typical fashion, Emily's dad, Mike, said, "I don't know. I just want you to get this whole thing done."

Emily's mom, on the other hand—much like Emily—had a lot of questions and concerns.

There were many things that were really important to her. I learned early on that Emily's mother had a seizure disorder and had not driven in 20 years. She had several essential medications. She had doctors she trusted and even a pharmacist she valued. She had built a strong relationship with her local pharmacist and didn't want to leave them. She was also very attached to certain doctors who were important to her. I knew right away that if we weren't able to get this trusted pharmacist, these dependable doctors, and these specific medications covered, it would be devastating for her.

I realized it was an important teaching moment—understanding that I had two spouses in front of me, each with completely different needs and concerns.

We sat down for a long conversation, about an hour and a half to two hours, and did a deep dive into each medication, each doctor, and which plan would best cover them.

We looked at which plan would allow her to continue using the mom-and-pop pharmacy in California that she had relied on for years. That pharmacy was a critical part of her routine, and I wanted to ensure she could continue going there without disruption.

What I want to convey here is that what's important to you is what's important to me as an agent. Now, there may be things that matter to you that might not be the best fit, and I will always be transparent in helping you understand why or why not. But in this scenario, it was crucial that we checked the boxes for Lynnie—medications, pharmacy, doctors—and made sure she had a plan that covered her holistically. We spent a lot of time focusing on her needs.

What's really cool about that is that every single year now, on Thanksgiving morning—before we sit down for our big Thanksgiving feast—

we go through it all over again. And we go through those same exact things for Lynnie every single year. We go through her medications. We go through her doctors. We go through her pharmacists, review all her different plans, and make sure that the plan that worked for her this year will still work for her next year. And sometimes, we make changes because Medicare is constantly evolving.

I found it incredibly fulfilling to help my family. It also helped me realize that so many people out there have the exact same concerns. They need to see the same doctor. They need to go to the same pharmacist. They need to make sure they're able to travel.

Emily's family lives in California, while we live in Tennessee. They spend about three months of the year in Tennessee, so they needed a plan that would provide excellent coverage in both states—and we were able to make that happen. Whether you're a homebody, traveling to see family, or have specific conditions that require specialized care, we'll find a plan that holistically meets all your needs.

As we wrap up the story of Lynnie and Mike, my current in-laws, I want to take you back into that situation and walk you through exactly how we teach, educate, and guide people through Medicare. We're going to break this down throughout this book at the simplest level possible, starting from the very beginning, to help you truly understand Medicare as a whole.

One thing I always urge people to do is get out a piece of paper and take notes. I think it's really important to highlight key points in this book and use it as an interactive resource. So many people bring this book into my office with sections highlighted.

That brings me back to one of the first questions I ask people: What is most important to you? Understanding that helps me recognize which points really resonated with you—or which ones didn't and need further explanation.

But right now, we're going to break this down from the most foundational part of Medicare: Original Medicare. That's where Medicare was founded, and everyone who enrolls in Medicare must have these two parts. If you're taking notes or highlighting, the letters you're going to hear over and over again are Medicare Part A and Part B.

And if we break this down even further, Medicare Part A is your hospital coverage, and Medicare Part B is your doctor coverage.

ORIGINAL MEDICARE
(PART A AND PART B)

PART A:
HOSPITAL COVERAGE

PART B:
DOCTOR COVERAGE

Figure 1.1

Let's take that even further. When we talk about Medicare Part A, which is hospital coverage, that's the coverage that kicks in when you have inpatient hospital stays. If you are staying overnight in a hospital, Medicare Part A will cover that for you.

Medicare Part A is often automatically provided when you turn 65, or you can sign up for it at 65, even if you're still working. Medicare Part B is your doctor's coverage or outpatient coverage.

Medicare Part A covers inpatient hospital stays, and Medicare Part B covers outpatient doctor visits. If you go to your primary care doctor, see a specialist, or receive any outpatient care, that will fall under Medicare Part B. That, again, is the foundation of Medicare. When you think about that red, white, and blue Medicare card, that's exactly what it says on there. You may even have one right now. And if you do, it will say Medicare Part A – Hospital and Medicare Part B – Medical (Doctor). If we think about Medicare like building a house, these two parts form the foundation. That is your concrete. That is what holds everything together—Medicare Part A and Medicare Part B.

The next question I often get is: "What does each part cost?" We've already covered what they include, so let's go over the costs.

Medicare Part A is traditionally premium-free.

That can be a little misleading because, if you check your payroll taxes, you'll see a Medicare deduction. If you're self-employed, you've been paying Medicare taxes. You've actually been contributing to Medicare throughout your working life.

As long as you've worked 40 quarters (10 years) or your spouse has worked 40 quarters (10 years), you will qualify for Medicare Part A at *no additional cost*. Again, you've already paid into it, but once you reach eligibility, there will be no further payments required for Part A. And again, Part A covers hospital care.

Part B, on the other hand, is your doctor and outpatient coverage, and it is not free. Almost everyone on Medicare must pay a Part B premium. In 2026, that premium is $202.90 per month for the standard income earner.

In rare situations, some individuals may qualify for assistance with their Part B premium. If you believe that might apply to you, I strongly encourage you to book a one-on-one appointment to determine eligibility. However, it's not common.

On the other hand, if you are a high-income earner, you may pay more for Part B. We see this quite often. If your adjusted gross income is above a certain threshold—around $109,000 if single of $218,000 if married filing jointly in 2026—you will be subject to an additional charge known as the Part B IRMAA (Income-Related Monthly Adjustment Amount).

I want to slow down here to ensure that you take note of this if it applies to you. If your adjusted gross income exceeds that threshold, you will pay more for your Medicare Part B coverage.

I recommend reviewing the current Medicare Part B premium and IRMAA guidelines to understand how your income may impact your costs. Be sure to bring this up during your one-on-one appointment so we can review it together and walk through what applies to your specific situation.

But for Part B, the number we're going to use in this book is the standard Part B premium, because that's what most people will pay.

The next topic is the enrollment scenario. Many people ask me, "Okay, Chase, I understand Medicare Part A and B. Medicare Part A covers the hospital, and Medicare Part B covers the doctor. But when do I enroll, and when do I get these benefits?"

If we go back to Lynnie and Mike, their situation was particularly interesting.

They were both enrolling in Part B at different times. Lynnie had already been enrolled in Medicare Part B because she qualified through Medicare disability. Mike, on the other hand, was 67 years old and had just decided to retire. He had delayed his Medicare Part B and was enrolling at a later time.

I don't want to confuse anyone here, but there are three different Medicare Part B enrollment scenarios that you may fall into. We'll include a diagram here to help clarify. The most important thing is identifying which category applies to you.

ORIGINAL MEDICARE ENROLLMENT SCENARIOS

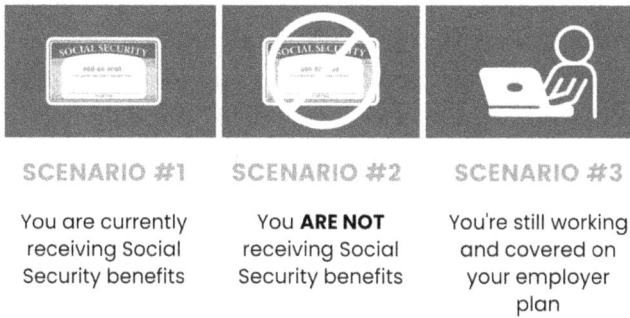

SCENARIO #1	SCENARIO #2	SCENARIO #3
You are currently receiving Social Security benefits	You **ARE NOT** receiving Social Security benefits	You're still working and covered on your employer plan

Figure 1.2

The easiest scenario, Scenario 1, is if you are turning 65 and already receiving Social Security. If you're already drawing Social Security benefits, you'll automatically be enrolled in Medicare Parts A and B. You'll receive your red, white, and blue Medicare card about three months before turning 65. While you have the option to delay Medicare Part B, this is uncommon for those already receiving Social Security. That's the simplest enrollment scenario.

Scenario 2 applies if you are no longer working and not drawing Social Security. If you're not working and not receiving Social Security benefits, you will likely need to enroll in Medicare Part B yourself. This is where we step in to help guide you through the process. There are several ways to enroll in Medicare—you can do it online, over the phone, in person, or by mail. No matter which method you choose, we will be there to help you, walk you through the options, and determine the easiest way for you to enroll based on your preference. So, again, refer back to the chart. If this scenario applies to you, circle it, or if you're taking notes, make sure you identify which enrollment category fits your situation.

The last scenario, and often the most complicated, is if you are still working, turning 65, not drawing Social Security, and trying to determine what's best for you. This is when meeting with a professional is the best approach. We will compare your group employer coverage with your Medicare options side by side and help you determine the best course of action. This is a case-by-case decision—not a one-size-fits-all solution. For some people, staying on their employer-sponsored insurance makes the most sense. For others, enrolling in Medicare is the better choice. Either way, it's critical that we analyze both options carefully and make an informed decision based on your needs.

As we wrap up these three scenarios, take a moment to identify which one applies to you. In Scenario 1, you're already drawing Social Security.

ORIGINAL MEDICARE ENROLLMENT SCENARIOS

SCENARIO 1: **If you currently receive Social Security benefits:**

- Automatically enrolled into Original Medicare
- Receive ID Card three months before birthday
  - Part B taken out of Social Security Check

Figure 1.3

When you turn 65 in Scenario 1, you're going to be enrolled in Medicare automatically.

In Scenario 2, you are not drawing Social Security, you are turning 65, and you are not working. In that scenario, we will most likely need to manually enroll you into Medicare.

ORIGINAL MEDICARE
ENROLLMENT SCENARIOS

SCENARIO 2: **If you currently DO NOT receive Social Security benefits:**
- You must **manually** enroll in Original Medicare
  - **Online** at: https://www.ssa.gov/benefits/medicare/
  - **Over the Phone:** 1-800-772-1213
  - **In person** at Social Security Office
  - **Mailing** in Application to Social Security
- (Part B) Billed quarterly

Figure 1.4

In Scenario 3, you're still working, you still have employer coverage, and we'll need to make a decision on which option is best for you. These are your three enrollment scenarios for going on to Original Medicare.

ORIGINAL MEDICARE
ENROLLMENT SCENARIOS

SCENARIO 3: **If you're still working and covered on your employer plan:**
1. Enroll in Medicare effective on your 65th Birthday

   OR
2. Delay Part B of your Medicare until you retire and get Part B then

Figure 1.5

Medicare Parts A and B are the foundation of the system. But just like building a house, a foundation alone isn't enough—you need more to complete the structure.

What do these leave you with? What exposures? What responsibilities are you left with when it comes to Medicare Parts A and B and not having anything else? Medicare Part A, again, is hospital coverage. On day 1, if you have Medicare Part A and you go into a hospital without any other coverage, you have a $1,736 deductible. After that, you're responsible for a daily co-pay during your hospital stay.

So that deductible will be paid on the front end, and then a daily co-pay if you have a longer hospital stay. A long term hospital stay could cost thousands if you only have Medicare Parts A and B. Medicare Part B, on the other hand, is your doctor and outpatient coverage.

A lot of people think of this as 20%—Medicare covers 80%, and you're responsible for 20%. That's partially true. Medicare Part B covers 80% of doctor visits, and you are responsible for 20% with no cap. At no point is there a max out-of-pocket. At no point is there a stopping point. You owe 20% with no limit. There's also a Medicare Part B deductible of $283 and some excess charges.

These are the foundational components of Medicare that we'll need to be aware of as we work through this conversation and understand why it's so important to have coverage that fills these gaps. Medicare Supplement plans and Medicare Advantage plans—you're probably getting a lot of solicitations for these right now—are designed to address these gaps. Medicare Parts A and B are the foundation for all of these options.

I want to wrap up this chapter by sharing a story about a couple of people I know who are also clients of mine. I get referrals all the time —friends of friends, neighbors, or people who were sent to me by someone they trust—but I really want to tell you about Barbara and John, who are clients of mine in Florida. When they came to me, they were already on Medicare, and Barbara had some serious chronic health issues. She had a Medicare Supplement plan, but she reached out to me because I had been highly recommended.

She was paying too much for her insurance, but because of her health issues, switching plans was not in her best interest. Even though there were less expensive options available, staying on her existing plan was the best choice for her health. John, on the other hand, was in great health, took very little medication, and had no major concerns. We were able to enroll him in a zero-premium Medicare Advantage plan, which he still has to this day.

He has had it for years and has had an exceptional experience with it. But I still remember that first phone call. Living in Florida (a very expensive market), Barbara told me, "Hey, my neighbor is only paying $100 a month," while she was paying almost $300. We went through the same process we did with Lynnie and Mike.

We sat down and went over her individual questions. I knew what was really important to her—price and coverage. It was one of those scenarios where she didn't like my recommendation, but it was in her best interest to keep her on the same plan, even though it wasn't associated with us, because it provided the best coverage for her.

She has continued to have a lot of health issues over the last four or five years, and the plan she's on has covered her exceptionally well. Even though she pays more than she would like, it was the best option for her. Her husband, John, on the other hand, often jokes during our annual reviews that he's paying nothing and saving so much money—mostly to get a rise out of Barbara.

But over the past five years, as we've worked together and had our annual reviews, they've come to understand that I truly treat them like family, making recommendations that are in their best interest—even when those recommendations aren't necessarily the most popular or preferred option. My job is to give you advice that you may not always like—but respect—because it comes from someone with a long track record of experience, a strong reputation, and the ability to make well-informed decisions on your behalf.

I truly appreciate working with Barbara and John, but I also think their situation serves as an important reminder that just because your neighbor is on a certain plan—because they were referred by Bob down the street, or because Bob was saving a couple hundred dollars a month—doesn't mean that plan is right for you. The key is to look at your specific needs.

As we move forward and continue educating and guiding you in this book, I want you to really understand that our focus is on your situation, your needs, and making the best recommendations for you.

CHAPTER 2

MEDICARE SUPPLEMENT VS. MEDICARE ADVANTAGE

A s we transition into chapter two and we've covered the foundation of Medicare—Parts A and B—I want to continue building on that analogy. As we put up the walls of that house, I want to talk about what most people come to us for: Medicare Supplement and Medicare Advantage plans. These are the next essential components of the house we're building together. Almost every single person I meet with comes to me without truly understanding the difference between a Medicare Supplement and a Medicare Advantage plan. Here's a quick visual of your Medicare coverage choices.

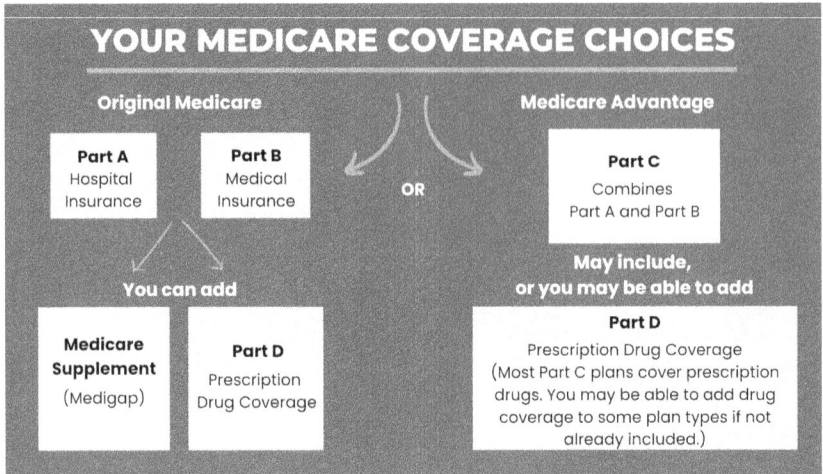

Figure 2.1

A lot of people think they understand the difference, while others are very upfront and admit they have no clue. I want to share an example from my most recent clients because, as I often say, almost every client fits into this mold. I draw comparisons from Catherine and Bill, two clients I met with this past week. They were just like anyone else I would meet with. They were referred by some longtime clients, but whether it's someone watching one of our webinars, attending one of our seminars, or meeting with us for the first time, I see this same scenario play out quite often.

With Catherine and Bill specifically, they came to me with the traditional questions. I asked, "What are the things you want to check off your list today?" and they gave me the usual items.

One thing that stood out to me was when they said, "Well, we want to talk about these zero-premium plans and these food cards and all these extra benefits."

I said, "Okay, great, you're referring to a Medicare Advantage plan."

They responded, "I thought that was a Medicare Supplement plan."

My point is that you might be feeling just as confused right now as they were, simply by hearing terms like Medicare Supplement, Medicare Advantage, food cards, and so on.

That's exactly the issue. People come to me overwhelmed by so much information, so many conflicting messages, that oftentimes, we just have to clear away everything they've heard and start from the beginning. That's exactly what I did with Catherine and Bill. As we sat down, they really couldn't explain to me what they were referring to, and I told them, "That's completely fine."

This happens all the time—people come to me with something they received in the mail, something they saw in an email, or something a friend mentioned, but they don't actually know what it means. And that's exactly why I have a job and why we've built a national practice with a strong reputation and countless reviews. We broke everything down, and as you continue writing on your piece of paper or taking notes, remember that there are two main options—two paths you can go down. Everything starts with Original Medicare, Parts A and B. That is the foundation of our house. We can't go anywhere without the foundation, or else the house falls apart.

This is precisely what I explained to Catherine and Bill as I sat with them. They were sitting right in front of me, and we walked through exactly what their options were, step by step, to figure out what would best cover the exposures we talked about.

I said, "Okay, Medicare Part A—that's your hospital coverage. Medicare Part B—that's your doctor coverage." I told them, "I want you to write down under Medicare Part A that you have an exposure of about $1,736 on day one if you're admitted to the hospital, and then you can have a per-day co-pay after that. A hospital stay could cost you thousands of dollars. Part B costs $202.90 a month, but you're still responsible for 20% of your medical expenses with no cap."

We wrote those two things down on a piece of paper. Then I looked at Catherine and Bill and asked, "Now, what's going to cover the rest of that?" And both of them said, "I don't know." That's where Medicare Supplement and Medicare Advantage plans come into play. If you have

Medicare, these are the two options you can choose to cover the remaining costs.

Some people also have a third option—employer coverage. If you have that option, we'll advise you on whether it's a viable or better choice for you. But for most people, these are the two primary options, and we're going to focus on them: Medicare Supplement and Medicare Advantage.

I want you to take a piece of paper and draw a line down the middle— just one straight line down the center, *hot dog style,* as we used to call it in elementary school. Now, on one side, write "Medicare Supplement," and on the other side, write "Medicare Advantage."

This is where the conversation begins. We're going to take a deep dive into each of these options and help you decide which one is best for you.

We'll start on the left-hand side. If you're taking notes, Medicare Supplement should be on the left, and Medicare Advantage should be on the right. There's no particular reason for this—it's just easier for me to start with Medicare Supplement since it was originally part of Medicare, while Medicare Advantage came later.

So, for Medicare Supplement, we know that no matter what, you have to pay the Medicare Part B premium. Whether you choose Medicare Supplement or Medicare Advantage, you can write "$202.90" on both sides of your paper—that's the monthly cost for Medicare Part B.

If you are drawing Social Security, your Medicare Part B premium will be automatically deducted from your Social Security payments. If you are not drawing Social Security, you will receive a bill from Social Security.

Each side of our paper should have $202.90. We know we are going to pay $202.90 either way, okay? Now, on the Medicare Supplement side, let's work our way down that list. Medicare Supplement plans are known for providing the most comprehensive, robust coverage.

If we go back to Lynnie, she has a Medicare Supplement plan. It provides her with top-notch coverage. She can see any doctor or hospital in the United States that accepts Medicare, which is virtually everyone. This was really important to Lynnie since she has some health concerns, and from the beginning, it was a clear no-brainer that a Medicare Supplement was the best option for her. Her plan allows her to see any doctor or hospital she wants, as long as they accept Medicare.

Now, if you're writing things down, you should have $202.90, and then next to it, write "comprehensive coverage, any doctor, any hospital that takes Medicare." Below that, add "Medicare Supplement."

Traditionally, Medicare Supplement plans come with a one-time-per-year deductible ($283 in 2026). That $283 is your Part B deductible, and once you pay it, your Medicare doctor and hospital services will be covered at 100%.

A Medicare Supplement plan also has an additional premium, which depends on your zip code. You're going to hear me talk about zip codes quite a bit in this book. Premiums, quotes, and plan designs are all based on your zip code. So, with a Medicare Supplement plan, you pay $202.90 for Part B, and then you have an additional premium for the supplement, which varies by location.

This plan offers the most robust coverage, allows you to see any doctor or hospital, and has no network restrictions as long as the provider accepts Medicare. It provides comprehensive coverage with a $283 deductible. Those are all things you should write down.

This picture is going to become very clear, I promise. You will also need to add prescription coverage if you want to avoid a penalty. The last thing to write down in this section is "Prescription Drug Coverage (Part D)."

I'll summarize this one last time. I know I'm repetitive, but that's what it takes to fully understand this. Repetition is key. You need to write this down and approach it like you're being coached and learning something new for the first time. When I was coaching, we did the same drills every day before practice to build muscle memory and reinforce the fundamentals.

That's exactly how I want to ensure you understand this. We have $202.90 written down for Medicare Part B. You have an additional premium for your Medicare Supplement—your no-network plan that lets you see any doctor or hospital as long as they take Medicare. And you also need a prescription plan.

Let's now transition to the right-hand side of the page—the Medicare Advantage plan. Medicare Advantage is newer to the scene and is a form of managed care, which we'll discuss further later in the book. It actually replaces Medicare Parts A and B, but you must still be enrolled in Medicare Part A and continue paying your Part B premium. When you choose a Medicare Advantage plan, you're enrolling in a managed care plan that provides your Medicare benefits.

These plans are often zero premium or have a very small premium. What attracts many people to these plans are the additional benefits they offer.

So, as we write on this page, start by writing $202.90, because we know we have to pay the Part B premium. After that, let's compare the networks side by side. Medicare Advantage plans typically have a more restrictive network.

They're PPO or HMO plans, and you'll need to see a doctor within the plan's network to get the best coverage or the best pricing. These plans have more restrictions and specific networks, but that's not necessarily a bad thing. Full transparency—we have thousands of people on both types of plans.

There is no one-size-fits-all solution, and both options can be great choices. The biggest difference is the cost, especially depending on where you are in the country. Some of these plans, as I mentioned, have a $0 premium, meaning you don't pay anything for them. That can mean significant savings on monthly premiums, and if you're on a budget, this may be one of your only options—so it's definitely a relevant conversation. I often compare these plans to group insurance coverage.

Medicare Advantage plans include co-pays, maximum out-of-pocket limits, deductibles, and co-insurance. This means they are more of a gamble when it comes to your healthcare costs. I can't tell you exactly what you'll pay out-of-pocket with these plans—it all depends on your health and the services you require.

So, as we write things down, start with $202.90. Then, note that you have a network-based plan, with premiums typically ranging from $0 to $50. After that, write down co-pays, max out-of-pocket costs, deductibles, and co-insurance. These are important factors to consider.

The last thing to write down here is extra benefits. These plans offer additional benefits, including dental, vision, hearing, gym memberships (such as SilverSneakers), and over-the-counter benefits. Medicare Supplement plans, on the other hand, do not offer these extra benefits.

A Medicare Supplement plan does not include dental, vision, or hearing coverage. Some plans may offer a gym membership, but most do not. There are clear differences between the two options.

Also, on the right-hand side of your page, under Medicare Advantage plans, note that prescription drug coverage is included, so you don't need to purchase an additional prescription plan. Below this, you'll find a cheat sheet chart summarizing this information in the hot dog-style format. You can reference that, but I strongly encourage you to write this down yourself and identify the questions that are most important to you.

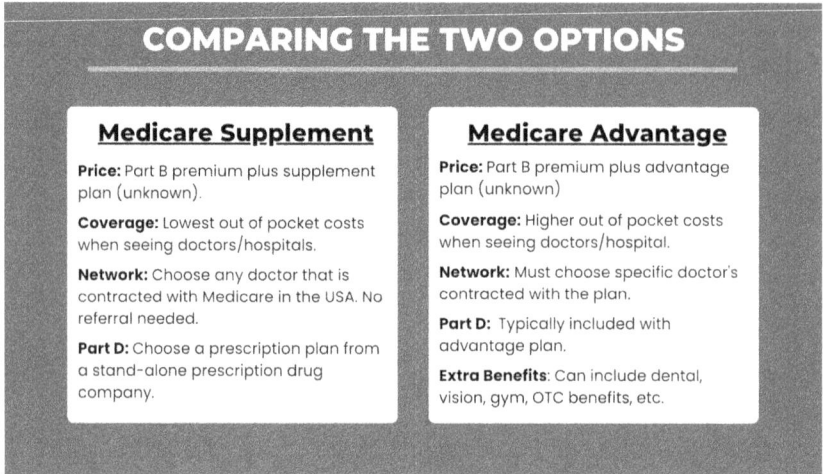

COMPARING THE TWO OPTIONS

Medicare Supplement

Price: Part B premium plus supplement plan (unknown).

Coverage: Lowest out of pocket costs when seeing doctors/hospitals.

Network: Choose any doctor that is contracted with Medicare in the USA. No referral needed.

Part D: Choose a prescription plan from a stand-alone prescription drug company.

Medicare Advantage

Price: Part B premium plus advantage plan (unknown)

Coverage: Higher out of pocket costs when seeing doctors/hospital.

Network: Must choose specific doctor's contracted with the plan.

Part D: Typically included with advantage plan.

Extra Benefits: Can include dental, vision, gym, OTC benefits, etc.

Figure 2.2

If I were in an elevator with you and had only 45 seconds to explain the difference between a Medicare Supplement plan and a Medicare Advantage plan, I would put it like this:

A Medicare Supplement plan costs more, but you get more. You take on less financial risk, your costs are predictable throughout the year, and you don't have to worry about unexpected medical expenses. You pay a little more upfront, but it provides peace of mind.

I always say that money changes hands when problems are solved. Medicare Supplement plans solve the problem of unpredictable healthcare costs, and you pay for that security.

Medicare Advantage plans, on the other hand, typically have little to no monthly cost, but if you need care, you'll be paying out-of-pocket —and in some cases, you could end up spending much more than if you had just chosen a Medicare Supplement plan in the first place.

Medicare Supplement plans don't include extra benefits, which may be a deciding factor for some people. It may also simply come down to budget. But, in short, with one option, you pay more and get more; with the other, you pay less but take on more financial exposure.

Sticking with our construction metaphor, we've started putting up the walls of the house, and we're beginning to build a solid educational understanding of Medicare Supplement and Medicare Advantage plans.

As we transition and wrap up this chapter, I want to touch on a couple of really important things that you'll hear us discuss throughout the book. The first is the importance of critical illness coverage—specifically, cancer, heart attack, and stroke coverage. Long story short, no matter which option you choose, we highly recommend adding a cancer, heart attack, and stroke rider.

There are a number of reasons for this, but the bottom line is that if you experience a cancer diagnosis, heart attack, or stroke, this is an area where Medicare will leave you with out-of-pocket expenses that your plan may or may not cover. We have clients who are diagnosed with these conditions every single day, and each one of them faces unexpected medical costs.

The next thing we're going to talk about is skilled nursing coverage.

One of the most important—and often overlooked—parts of Medicare and retirement planning is skilled care, nursing coverage, and home care. This is one of the biggest threats to your financial security. The only way to protect yourself from the costs of a nursing home or skilled care claim is to have a plan in place—unless you plan to self-pay, which could deplete your assets or put you in a Medicaid spend-down situation that could even take your home away. You need a plan in place.

What you need to know is that Medicare only covers up to 100 days of skilled care. That is the maximum coverage you can receive through Medicare. After those 100 days, there is absolutely nothing that covers you except a private plan.

If you take away anything from this book, make sure you understand the importance of protecting yourself from a $7,000, $8,000, or even $10,000 per month nursing home bill, depending on the facility and level of care. The last thing I'm going to show you in this chapter is our umbrella coverage options. We have three different umbrella options.

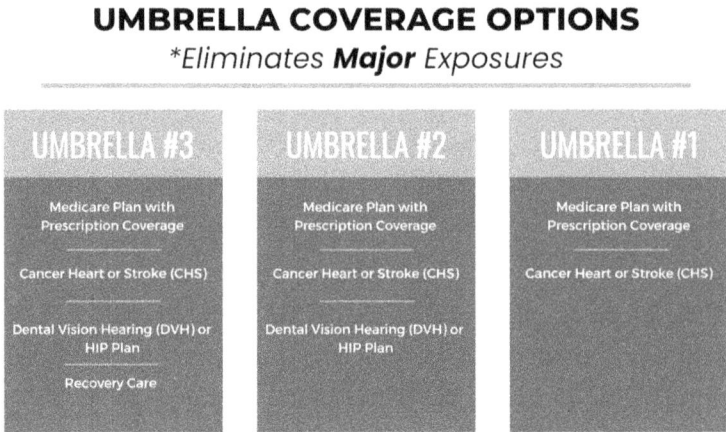

UMBRELLA COVERAGE OPTIONS
*Eliminates **Major** Exposures*

UMBRELLA #3	UMBRELLA #2	UMBRELLA #1
Medicare Plan with Prescription Coverage	Medicare Plan with Prescription Coverage	Medicare Plan with Prescription Coverage
Cancer Heart or Stroke (CHS)	Cancer Heart or Stroke (CHS)	Cancer Heart or Stroke (CHS)
Dental Vision Hearing (DVH) or HIP Plan	Dental Vision Hearing (DVH) or HIP Plan	
Recovery Care		

Figure 2.3

These are going to eliminate these additional exposures—cancer, heart attack, stroke, nursing home, dental, hospital expenses, and more. This is how you cover the major costs that Medicare alone will not cover. We'll go into more detail throughout the book, but it's helpful to briefly introduce them here in Chapter 2.

Lastly, I want to finish this chapter with a story about Larry and his wife, Laurie.

I first knocked on their door in 2018. They were very wealthy, lived in an affluent neighborhood, and they have been great clients of mine. I love talking to them every year.

When I sat down with them, Laurie was focused on getting the best coverage in place. She chose a Medicare Supplement plan, and as I got to know her, it was clear she was the leader in making their healthcare decisions. There's always one spouse who takes the lead in making these kinds of decisions, and for them, it was Laurie. She has always been super pleasant and easy to work with, and I look forward to our conversations each year. We talk about football, we talk about family, and we even vacation in the same parts of the country.

I enjoy talking to Larry too, but for completely different reasons. Larry is the kind of guy who has been very successful in life and does things his own way. I respect that. I had always given him my best advice, but Larry was one of those people who, even if you gave him the right advice, would still do things his own way.

Larry decided in 2019 that he was going to go without a Medicare Supplement or Medicare Advantage plan. He didn't want to pay any additional money and didn't think he needed to protect himself from any financial exposure. He was wealthy and believed he could cover anything on his own. I think you can see where this story is going.

In 2023, Larry was diagnosed with leukemia. Leukemia requires a very specific set of medications and treatments. These medications require Part B coverage. So again, if we go back to that Part B coverage, Larry only had 80% covered—he was responsible for 20% with no cap.

Larry ended up paying tens of thousands of dollars. He could afford it at the time, and he still could, but the first person he called was me. He asked me what his options were and even apologized. He said, "I should have gone with something."

He realized he wasn't invincible and should have had some type of coverage. But at that point, the only option we could offer him was a Medicare Advantage plan, as he was no longer healthy enough to qualify for a Medicare Supplement. He had made a critical mistake in our original meeting by choosing to do nothing.

For anyone reading this book, that's exactly what I urge you not to do: make sure you do *something*. There are free plans available. There are different options for every scenario. But the worst thing you can do is nothing.

I still talk with Larry and Laurie every year. We have the best possible plan in place for Larry now, but it could have been better. And that's my point: by being proactive and taking action early, you can put yourself in a much better position.

CHAPTER 3
MEDICARE SUPPLEMENTS DEEP DIVE

I want to start this chapter by sharing some of my experiences over the last ten years. It's wild to think that at only 35—going on 36—I've already been doing this for over a decade.

I have had a unique perspective, seeing many people transition into different stages of their lives. I work with a lot of people when they turn 65, and I also work with many who come to me well past that age. Over the past 10 years, I have witnessed a lot of change.

I've seen people's health deteriorate, I've seen unfortunate health events, and I've seen people near the end of their lives. With that, I've also seen how their coverage works when they need it most.

Cancer, heart attacks, strokes, death—seeing how families have to navigate claims during those critical moments has been incredibly eye-opening. One thing I can confidently say is that the Medicare Supplement plan we're about to discuss is the most comprehensive and robust option available.

We talked about it throughout the last chapter, and when you have this coverage, it leaves you with the least amount of worry, the least amount of anxiety, and the best protection when you need it most. It reminds me of one of my very first clients—who, sadly, passed away a few weeks ago.

She was literally my first client ever. I remember the date—January 9, 2016. I had just started with a small company, and they told us to go knock on doors. They handed me a list of people turning 65.

I knocked on Steve and Fran Ford's door. They were living in Auburn, Illinois, at the time. It was a cold day, and it was snowing.

Steve was so kind, and Fran was incredibly gracious. They welcomed me right in. On the very first day I started this job, they purchased a Medicare Supplement plan from me.

Every year from then on, I met with them for an annual review. I sat at their kitchen table. I remember bringing them lunch from La Gondola sub shop after they moved to Decatur, Illinois. That's another thing—I see a lot of people move, and when they do, I move with them.

I can still picture sitting at their table in Decatur over the last few years. Then, about three weeks ago, I got a call. Someone from their church reached out and said, "Hey, Fran passed away. I know she was your first client, and I know they were important to you." I get a little emotional even thinking about it now—seeing that transition in life. I was Facebook friends with them. I saw the obituary. But where I'm going with this story is that Fran had a Medicare Supplement plan.

She had a multiple-week hospital stay. She had heart failure. She went through so much. But what she didn't have was a bill.

Through all of life's transitions, I may have just been "the insurance guy," but in a time when they needed coverage the most—and in an incredibly difficult time for the family—that coverage did its job. It left the family with no added stress, no unexpected financial burden, and ensured Fran received the best care possible as she neared the end of her life.

It's a story I will always look back on, and Steve remains a very close client of mine.

You always remember your first client, especially when you have thousands now. It's crazy to look back and see the impact of what you're really doing with these Medicare Supplement plans. As I mentioned, my father-in-law, Mike, and my mother-in-law, Lynnie, have these plans. I know that at the end of the day, when someone has a Medicare Supplement, they are going to receive the best care possible when they need it most.

I want to thank you for letting me share that story. It's one that is very close to me. Now, we'll transition into another story—one that's a little less heavy but still very important for you, as the reader, to understand.

After working with thousands of Medicare beneficiaries over the last decade, one of the most common issues I see—and one of the most common types of clients I meet—is someone over 65 who is paying too much for a Medicare Supplement plan. I see this all the time. Our team sees it daily. Long story short, if you have been on Medicare and have a Medicare Supplement, chances are you're overpaying for it.

One of the most overlooked aspects of Medicare is the assumption that just because you purchased a plan when you turned 65—or have been on it for a couple of years—that there isn't a better plan or a lower price available for you.

And probably the hardest part of my job is helping people understand that just because they have a Medicare Supplement—whether it's Plan G or Plan N (we'll talk a lot about Plan G and Plan N in this chapter)—doesn't mean there isn't an identical plan available for them at a much lower cost. What we see time and time again is people overpaying for the coverage they already have.

So I urge you, if you are already on a Medicare Supplement, to consider reviewing your options. This is one of the easiest changes to make. We're not changing your coverage—we're simply seeing if the same coverage is available at a lower price. That's something we do every day, and I want to make sure you, as the reader, know that you have that opportunity. It doesn't have to be during Medicare's open enrollment period—you can review and switch at any time throughout the year.

As we transition, we're going to take a deep dive into Medicare Supplement plans.

In the last chapter, we compared Medicare Supplements and Medicare Advantage plans side by side. Now, after hearing these stories and going through the pre-education from the last chapter, some of you may have already decided that a Medicare Supplement is the right choice for you. Or maybe you've done some research and are leaning toward a Medicare Supplement. Whatever the case may be, if you're considering a Medicare Supplement plan, we're going to focus in and help you understand it as thoroughly as possible.

I want to start by reviewing Medicare's biggest cost exposures. So again, remember—and you can refer to the chart that follows—Medicare Part A is your hospital coverage. In 2026, if you have a hospital stay and only have Medicare Parts A and B (with no additional coverage), you will have a $1,736 deductible for Medicare Part A, followed by a daily co-pay if you have a long -term hospitalization.

Now, Medicare Part B provides about 80% coverage—but you are responsible for the remaining 20% with no limit. Additionally, you have a deductible and some excess charges.

MAJOR EXPOSURES OF ORIGINAL MEDICARE

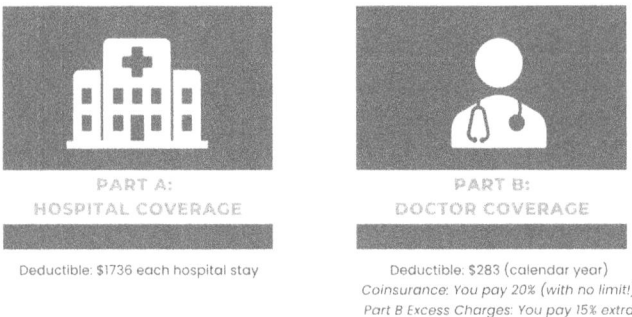

PART A: HOSPITAL COVERAGE	PART B: DOCTOR COVERAGE
Deductible: $1736 each hospital stay	Deductible: $283 (calendar year)
	Coinsurance: You pay 20% (with no limit!)
	Part B Excess Charges: You pay 15% extra

Figure 3.1

Now—drum roll—if you have a Medicare Supplement, that is what's called your secondary insurance and essentially plugs those gaps up. It covers those major exposures. Original Medicare is primary; that's your red, white, and blue card. Your Medicare Supplement comes in behind that and covers up those gaps, and you have what's called Original Medicare, and you are covered comprehensively. You can see a schematic of this in the next image. You have Original Medicare, you have your Medicare Supplement, and then most people would have a prescription plan that we'll talk about in the next chapter. Those three things combined are what Original Medicare was built on. That was the only option available until Medicare Advantage plans hit the scene.

OPTION 1: ORIGINAL MEDICARE

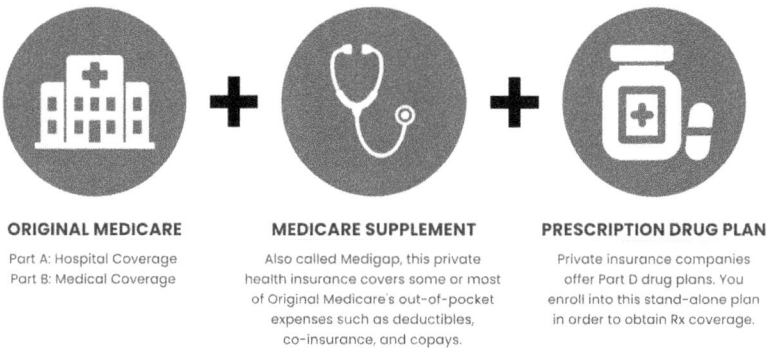

ORIGINAL MEDICARE	MEDICARE SUPPLEMENT	PRESCRIPTION DRUG PLAN
Part A: Hospital Coverage Part B: Medical Coverage	Also called Medigap, this private health insurance covers some or most of Original Medicare's out-of-pocket expenses such as deductibles, co-insurance, and copays.	Private insurance companies offer Part D drug plans. You enroll into this stand-alone plan in order to obtain Rx coverage.

Figure 3.2

This is really the foundation of Medicare, and it was the only available version at one time. What we're gonna do now is really take that middle circle there, the Medicare Supplement, and focus on that. Medicare Supplement; we've heard that term many times throughout this book so far. Now, when it comes to Medicare Supplement plans, numerous questions arise: What are they? How many are available? How do I choose one? What are all the different things I need to know? We're going to tackle that here.

The following chart is from your *Medicare and You Handbook*. This is from the official government handbook, and this chart shows you all the different Medicare Supplement plans available. This is where I see it—when somebody sits across from me, they get a little overwhelmed and say, "There are so many different options."

Medicare Supplement Insurance (Medigap) plans									
Benefits	A	B	C	D	F*	G	K	L	M	N
Medicare Part A coinsurance and hospital costs (up to an additional 365 days after Medicare benefits are used)	100%	100%	100%	100%	100%	100%	100%	100%	100%	100%
Medicare Part B coinsurance or copayment	100%	100%	100%	100%	100%	100%	50%	75%	100%	100%***
Blood (first 3 pints)	100%	100%	100%	100%	100%	100%	50%	75%	100%	100%
Part A hospice care coinsurance or copayment	100%	100%	100%	100%	100%	100%	50%	75%	100%	100%
Skilled nursing facility care coinsurance			100%	100%	100%	100%	50%	75%	100%	100%
Part A deductible		100%	100%	100%	100%	100%	50%	75%	50%	100%
Part B deductible			100%		100%					
Part B excess charges					100%	100%				
Foreign travel emergency (up to plan limits)			80%	80%	80%	80%			80%	80%
							Out-of-pocket limit in 2020**			
							$5,880	$2,940		

Figure 3.3

Well, if you're writing, you can go ahead and cross out some plans, or what I would actually do is just circle these plans: Plan F, G, and N. Those are the only plans I ever see anyone on. Over the last decade, I can count on one hand how many people have had a Medicare Supplement that wasn't a Plan F, G, or N. These are the most popular plans. Additionally, if you are going on Medicare after January 1, 2020, you cannot choose a Plan F, so that one is not even an option for you.

That leaves you with a Plan G and a Plan N. If you went on Medicare prior to January 1, 2020, you can still choose Plan F. As we really zoom in on these for the purpose of this book, we're going to focus on Plan G and Plan N because they are relevant to everyone reading. As you look through the coverage on the graph, Plan G covers almost 100% of the co-insurance of all Medicare expenses, except for the Medicare Part B deductible. To make it simple, your supplement is going to cover essentially 100% of Medicare-approved charges after you satisfy your annual deductible of $283.

We discussed that earlier, but go ahead and write it down. Your Medicare Part B deductible is $283 in 2026, and that is not to be confused with your Medicare Part B premium. Your Medicare Part B premium is what you pay the government, and that is $202.90 in 2026.

Everybody has to pay the Medicare Part B premium no matter what you do. Plan N, as we work our way to the end of the graph, is going to be very similar to Plan G. You have the same deductible, but now you have what's called excess charges. And again, let's really simplify this.

This is the part where, if you're writing things down, it's going to be really helpful just to take some notes and reference them. With a plan N Medicare Supplement, you could pay a small co-pay if you see a doctor or go to an emergency room. And then the excess charge is a small additional cost if the doctor charges more than the Medicare-approved amount. We'll break that down even further. As we work our way through the previous chart, you can see the section on skilled nursing co-insurance.

Look at the fifth row from the top, along the list of benefits on the left —skilled nursing coverage. I cannot stress this enough. If you take away anything from this book, it's that skilled nursing, nursing homes, and assisted living are where Medicare leaves you with the biggest financial exposures. Long story short, as shown in the illustration, after 100 days in a skilled nursing facility, nursing home, or rehabilitation center, you are completely on your own.

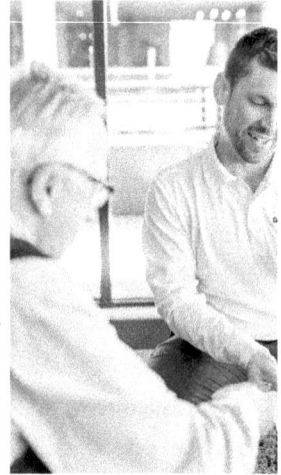

SKILLED NURSING COVERAGE

In each benefit period you pay:

- Days 1 - 20: $0 copayment (Note: if you are on a Medicare Advantage Plan, you may be charged co-payments during the first 20 days.)
- Days 21–100: $217 each day
- After day 100: all costs

Part A limits SNF coverage to 100 days in each benefit period.

Note: Your doctor or other health care provider may recommend you get services more often than Medicare covers. Or, they may recommend services that Medicare doesn't cover. If this happens, you may have to pay some or all of the costs. Ask questions so you understand why your doctor is recommending certain services and if, or how much, Medicare will pay for them.

Figure 3.4

You heard that correctly. If you have an extended stay beyond 100 days and do not have a private plan, you will have to pay out-of-pocket. And even getting those 100 days of coverage is extremely complicated.

To qualify for any coverage at all, you must have a three-day hospital admission. Then, to continue receiving coverage, you must show improvement in your condition.

Regardless of these factors, after 100 days, Medicare stops paying, and you either have to self-pay or find an alternative plan. Many people don't fully understand their options. The reality is that you either need to have a plan in place or be prepared to self-pay. When I say self-pay, that means using your 401(k), retirement savings, or cash in the bank.

If you don't have assets to cover the costs, you may have to go through a Medicaid spend-down, which can include losing your home or other valuable assets.

Situations like these can significantly impact the legacy you leave behind. That's why it's so important to consider umbrella coverage, which includes skilled care, home care, and nursing home coverage. This should be a priority. We never recommend any of these plans without also discussing umbrella coverage to protect against these major financial risks.

The next question I commonly get when people begin their Medicare journey is: How much does all of this cost? How much does a supplement cost? How much does umbrella coverage cost? What is the overall cost? Great question.

The first thing I'll ask for is your zip code. I can give you an average cost, but prices vary widely. On the low end, a Medicare Supplement plan costs around $100 per month. On the high end, it can be $200 per month. Again, it all depends on your zip code. We are licensed in all 50 states, helping people across the country, and pricing varies significantly from state to state and even zip code to zip code. It wouldn't be fair to give you a hard number right here.

Now, as we analyze the two Medicare Supplement plans, remember, we are focusing on Plan G and Plan N because they are relevant to everyone. Plan G, again, typically ranges from $100 to $200 per month.

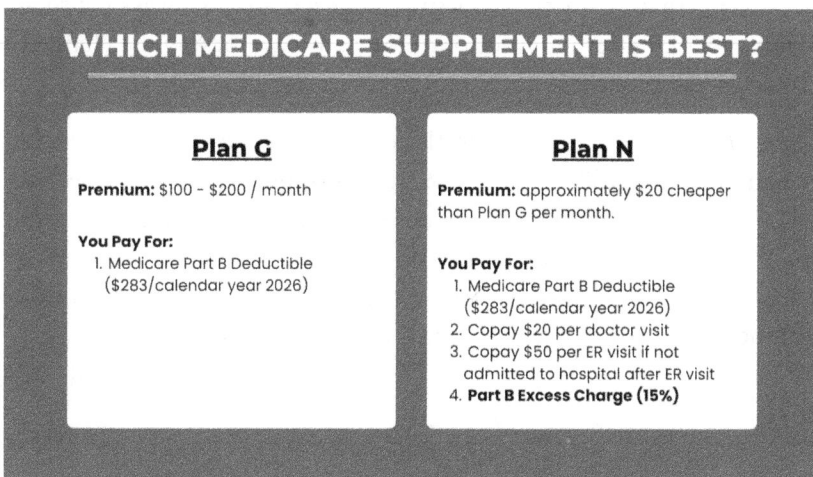

WHICH MEDICARE SUPPLEMENT IS BEST?

Plan G

Premium: $100 - $200 / month

You Pay For:
1. Medicare Part B Deductible ($283/calendar year 2026)

Plan N

Premium: approximately $20 cheaper than Plan G per month.

You Pay For:
1. Medicare Part B Deductible ($283/calendar year 2026)
2. Copay $20 per doctor visit
3. Copay $50 per ER visit if not admitted to hospital after ER visit
4. **Part B Excess Charge (15%)**

Figure 3.5

And essentially, as we talked about, that will cover your Medicare-approved expenses after Medicare A and B. So it supplements your

Medicare Part A and Part B coverage, paying for the remainder of your Medicare-approved expenses after you pay your annual deductible of $283.

Now, for Plan N, we talked about how it differs slightly. Traditionally, I think a good estimate is that Plan N saves you around $20 to $40 per month compared to Plan G.

By choosing Plan N, you take on slightly more financial exposure. However, many people prefer Plan N because the lower premium leaves room in their budget for umbrella coverage—such as skilled nursing, home care, cancer, heart attack, and stroke riders, as well as a dental plan. These additional coverages help fill the gaps Medicare leaves behind.

So many people like Plan N. Now, Plan N is going to have the same Medicare Part B deductible. It also has a small co-pay for a doctor visit and a small co-pay for an emergency room visit if you're admitted—$20 for a doctor visit and $50 for an emergency room visit.

I tell people all the time that many of my clients on Plan N report back to me that their doctor doesn't charge a co-pay. I always tell them, "Don't go asking for it." A lot of times, you may not even be charged a co-pay—it's up to the doctor.

Then, the excess charge, in bold there at the bottom—it says 15%, but remember, that's 15% of the 20%. If we do some quick math, let's say your bill was $1,000. Medicare covers 80%, leaving you responsible for 20%, which is $200. If the doctor applies an excess charge, it's 15% of that $200, which is $30. At the end of the day, even as those numbers add up, the excess charge is still relatively small.

KEY POINTS ABOUT MEDICARE SUPPLEMENTS

Best Time to Enroll

Six (6) months prior to your birthday month!
- Cheapest rates
- Avoid mistakes
- Check it off your list

Standardized Plans
- Supplements are federally regulated
- Coverage follows the letter of the plan NOT the company offering it
- Plan G coverage from company "A" is exactly the same coverage as Plan G from company "X", "Y", or "Z".

Figure 3.6

If you're going on Medicare for the first time, I strongly recommend doing this six months before you turn 65. That way, you lock in the lowest rates possible. One thing I always tell clients is that Medicare Supplement plans don't decrease in price. Insurance, in general, rarely sees rate reductions. Prices typically go up. The best time to enroll is six months prior, when you can secure the lowest rates available. This can actually lock in your rate for up to 18 months, and it helps you avoid costly mistakes.

If you start six months ahead, you also have time to fix any errors. Number one, if a mistake happens, we have plenty of time to correct it. Number two, pre-planning helps prevent mistakes in the first place. I've had clients enroll six months before turning 65, and I've had others wait until six days before. I promise you—the ones who do it six months ahead are far less stressed than those scrambling at the last minute. I urge you to begin the process as close to that six-month mark as possible.

And lastly, just check it off your list. We all have lingering to-do lists, but this process is actually much simpler when you have a trusted agency and an experienced agent guiding you.

Again, I want to remind you about the standardization of these plans. One example I always use is this: if you go to your local grocery store and buy a 12-pack of Coca-Cola, and then go across the street to Walmart and buy another 12-pack of Coca-Cola, what do you have? The exact same 12-pack. They were probably even delivered by the same truck. But the price you pay will likely be different. That's exactly what happens with Medicare Supplement plans. You can choose Company A, B, C, or D. For example, you could choose a Blue Cross supplement, or you could choose Cigna or Mutual of Omaha. All of these companies offer the exact same plan—the only difference is the price.

And that's one of the hardest things for people to understand. As discussed earlier in the chapter, even clients with substantial financial knowledge struggle to grasp that the insurance carrier does not provide any additional benefits or better coverage. These plans are standardized. The federal government mandates which plans insurance companies can offer and what coverage they must provide. The only thing the carriers control is the price.

So we have a list of companies here, and there are many different options to choose from. I just want to make it very clear: *we work for you, not the insurance company.* Our job is to represent all these companies independently and find the best plan for you and your needs.

As we start to wrap up this chapter, I think it's important to address some common myths about working with a Medicare broker or agency —especially from someone who has been educating people on Medicare for over 10 years.

The first myth is that you have to pay the agent. I've had many people in the past come to me and ask, "How much do I owe you?" or "How much does this cost?" I tell them, "Absolutely nothing," and they often look at me, completely surprised.

MYTH #1

"I must have to pay a fee to use a broker and get their help with all this"

TRUTH

We charge you no fees of any kind for our services!

Figure 3.7

First, charging a fee would be illegal. Second, the insurance companies pay us—not you.

That leads to myth number two: "Nobody works for free, so the insurance company must charge a higher price if I go through someone like you."

MYTH #2

"Nobody works for free, so the insurance company must charge a higher price if I go through a broker like you."

TRUTH

You will pay exactly the same price whether you use our help throughout this process or do it alone. The insurance companies pay us directly for educating you and helping you enroll.

Figure 3.8

Absolutely false. I cannot say this enough: you will pay the exact same price whether you work with a broker or do everything on your own.

The only difference is that without a broker, you wouldn't have an expert by your side to help guide you through changes year after year. And that is often the most overlooked benefit of using a broker.

Do big changes happen in Medicare? Absolutely. I talk to thousands of clients, and most have no idea what's changed since our last conversation. Having someone who stays on top of these changes—and who can help you adjust accordingly—is invaluable. And again, you don't have to pay a single penny for it.

Myth number three: "If you get paid by the insurance companies, you must be biased toward one company over another."

Completely false. This is exactly why we represent so many different plans. We work for you, not the insurance company.

MYTH #3

"If you get paid by the insurance companies, you must have a bias towards one company or the next."

TRUTH

We have access to over 25 different companies and get paid by whichever one you choose, so we aren't bias towards one company over another.

Figure 3.9

At the end of the day, if you came to me and said, "I want Company X," I would say, "That's fine." But if Company Z offers the exact same coverage at a lower price, I would point that out to you. If you still choose Company X, I'm not going to argue with you. Again, I work for you—not the insurance company.

My job is to educate you. My job is to ensure you have the best plan at the best price for your needs. But ultimately, the decision is yours.

And I'll be here, year after year, to help you make those decisions.

So to summarize:

- Truth number one: There are no fees charged.
- Truth number two: The price you pay the insurance company is the same with or without a broker.
- Truth number three: With over 25 companies to choose from, there is no bias in plan selection.

THREE TRUTHS OF USING A BROKER

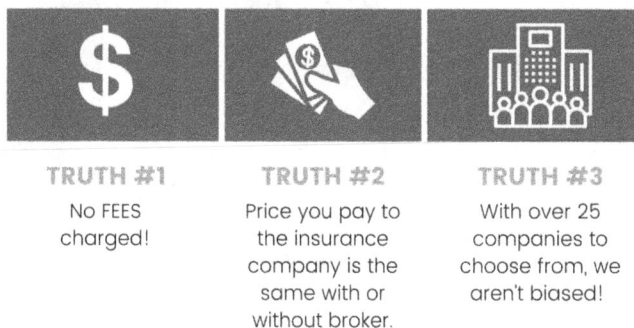

TRUTH #1	TRUTH #2	TRUTH #3
No FEES charged!	Price you pay to the insurance company is the same with or without broker.	With over 25 companies to choose from, we aren't biased!

Figure 3.10

To close this chapter, I look back on the last 10 years and think about Steve and Fran's story, along with the thousands of people we've helped with Medicare Supplement plans. At the end of the day, I know that when someone chooses a Medicare Supplement, they are going to have peace of mind.

They will have the best coverage when they need it and the ability to see the doctor or provider of their choice.

As you finish this chapter, I urge you to consider whether a Medicare Supplement is the right plan for you. Are you leaning toward Plan G or Plan N? Which umbrella coverage best fits your needs? I cannot say this enough—having the right plan in place makes all the difference.

The umbrella coverage, again, helps cover Medicare's major exposures, including skilled nursing, home care, critical illness coverage for cancer, heart attack, and stroke, as well as additional dental coverage if needed. The next image is the umbrella coverage chart. We also discussed the Medicare Supplement chart.

UMBRELLA COVERAGE OPTIONS
*Eliminates **Major** Exposures

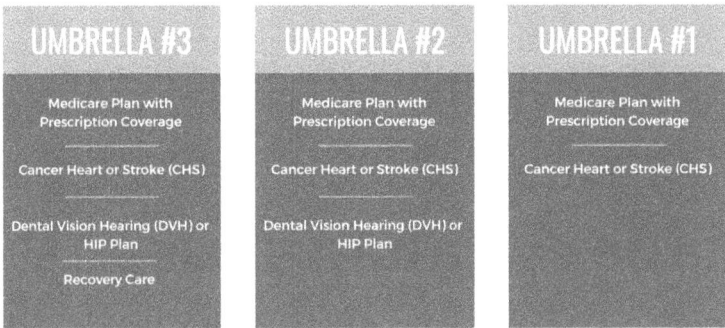

UMBRELLA #3	UMBRELLA #2	UMBRELLA #1
Medicare Plan with Prescription Coverage	Medicare Plan with Prescription Coverage	Medicare Plan with Prescription Coverage
Cancer Heart or Stroke (CHS)	Cancer Heart or Stroke (CHS)	Cancer Heart or Stroke (CHS)
Dental Vision Hearing (DVH) or HIP Plan	Dental Vision Hearing (DVH) or HIP Plan	
Recovery Care		

Figure 3.11

Make sure you identify that. Make sure you write it down. We look forward to going over your notes with you when you book a one-on-one meeting.

CHAPTER 4
PRESCRIPTION DRUG COVERAGE

I want to start this chapter on prescription drug coverage with a quick story (you know how much we love stories). I'm going to take you back to Larry.

Larry, if you remember, is one of my wealthier clients. He and Laurie have been longtime clients, and they have always been very particular about the way they do things. When we sat down to discuss Medicare, Laurie was quick to choose a Medicare Supplement plan and a Prescription Drug plan.

Larry, on the other hand, didn't feel the need for additional coverage and specifically didn't want to enroll in a drug plan because it would cost him extra. He didn't want to pay for something he didn't think he needed. At the time, he wasn't taking any medications—he was very healthy.

That's often the case when someone turns 65. Many people who enroll in Medicare have been active and healthy their entire lives. But the fact is, as we age, our health deteriorates, and at some point, we are likely to need medical attention.

Larry was no different. However, he decided at the time that he didn't want to take prescription drug coverage, which is fine. I have people all the time who choose not to take a drug plan.

But as we mentioned in previous chapters, Larry was eventually diagnosed with leukemia, which requires costly medical care and prescription treatments. One of the first things Larry did was call me. He explained his situation and told me about his diagnosis.

And then he admitted, in his own words, "I was dumb for not taking prescription drug coverage."

I don't fault Larry for his decision at the time. You don't know what you don't know. Nobody expects to be diagnosed with leukemia. But looking back, simply enrolling in a drug plan would have saved him a lot of trouble.

By the time he called me, he was already halfway through the year, and he couldn't enroll in prescription drug coverage until the next annual enrollment period (October through December). Even then, the new plan wouldn't take effect until January.

That meant Larry had to go the rest of the year without prescription coverage—while now being prescribed very expensive medications. This is exactly what I caution you, the reader, to be aware of. With prescription drug coverage, with Medicare, and with any kind of insurance, you are essentially protecting yourself against such unforeseen eventualities. Larry didn't want to believe he would need expensive prescriptions, but when the unexpected happened, he was left paying the price.

The long story short is that we now have Larry on a Prescription Drug plan, but he went four or five years without one—and that ended up costing him. He had to pay for extremely expensive medications out-of-pocket. And now, because he didn't enroll when he was first eligible, he also has a late enrollment penalty, which we'll discuss in a moment.

The point of this story is simple: If you choose not to take prescription drug coverage, that's fine, but you need to understand the risk. If you don't have coverage when you need it, you could end up in a difficult situation. This is something that we can easily prevent by discussing it in our initial meeting.

The main thing is just to make sure you're knowledgeable about these things. Let's talk through these things together. And let's make sure that you have the right plan and protection in place for the unforeseen events.

It's easy to plan for things we know are coming. It's much harder to plan for things we never expect. And that's exactly what happened with Larry. We were planning for something he had never even considered would happen to him. And that's something I see often in this profession.

When enrolling in Medicare, it's important to understand how prescription drug coverage fits into your healthcare plan. Original Medicare (Part A and Part B) covers hospital and medical services, but it does not include coverage for most prescription medications.

To ensure you have access to the medications you need, you can enroll in a stand-alone Prescription Drug Plan (PDP)—also known as Medicare Part D—which is offered by private insurance companies. However, Medigap plans do not include drug coverage. That's why enrolling in a separate Part D plan is critical for ensuring you have prescription coverage and avoid penalties.

By combining these three components—Original Medicare, a Medicare Supplement, and a Prescription Drug Plan—you create a comprehensive healthcare plan that covers hospital care, doctor visits, and necessary medications. Note that if you choose to go the Medicare Advantage route (which we will discuss in more detail in the next chapter), it often includes prescription drug coverage.

PRESCRIPTION DRUG COVERAGE

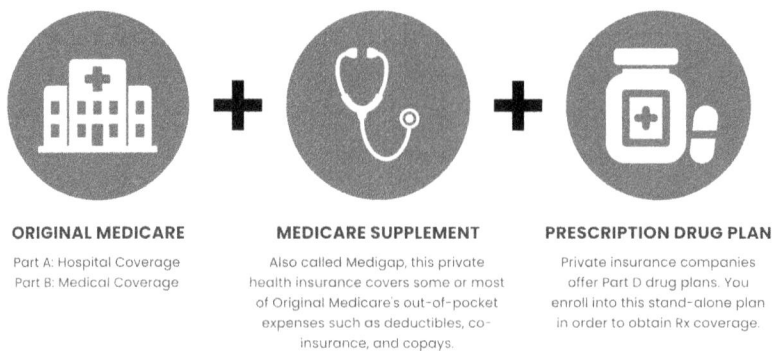

ORIGINAL MEDICARE

Part A: Hospital Coverage
Part B: Medical Coverage

MEDICARE SUPPLEMENT

Also called Medigap, this private
health insurance covers some or most
of Original Medicare's out-of-pocket
expenses such as deductibles, co-
insurance, and copays.

PRESCRIPTION DRUG PLAN

Private insurance companies
offer Part D drug plans. You
enroll into this stand-alone plan
in order to obtain Rx coverage.

Figure 4.1

Here, I really want to focus on its key components. And I want to caution you—the reader—that it's easy to get lost in the details of Part D prescription drug coverage. My goal in this chapter is to make it as simple and easy to understand as possible.

Most people take prescription drugs. But everyone takes different ones. Your neighbor is taking different prescriptions than you. Your best friend is taking different prescribed medications than you. Even your own spouse may be taking different prescriptions than you. While this won't be an individualized conversation, I want to break down the components of a Prescription Drug plan and highlight some key changes.

The first thing to understand is the components of a Prescription Drug plan.

The first and most obvious component is the premium you pay for your Prescription Drug plan. Almost every Prescription Drug plan comes with a monthly premium, which you'll pay in addition to your Part B or any other premiums. The cost of your Prescription Drug plan depends on the plan you choose and your zip code. The first step we take is to enter your zip code to see what prescription plans are available in your area. The second step is entering your prescriptions.

When we input your prescriptions, they will be matched to the plan's formulary—which is the list of drugs that the plan covers and how it covers them. The two key factors thus far are premium and formulary. The formulary is essential because it determines how your specific medications are covered under a given plan.

Next, there is a co-insurance or co-pay—which is the amount you pay when you fill a prescription. This is pretty self-explanatory.

Finally, many plans have a deductible—the amount you must pay before your plan begins to cover some or all of your medication costs.

These are the four major components of a Prescription Drug plan: premium, formulary, co-insurance or co-pay, and deductible. We will tie all of these together as we continue.

I want to quickly walk you through our extremely straightforward process. We make this super simple. The first thing we're going to do is use Medicare.gov's online calculator. If you're reading this, you can pause, go to Medicare.gov, enter your zip code, and type in your prescriptions. That's exactly what I do—I input your prescription drugs into the system. It doesn't matter if you have two prescriptions or twenty; we will enter them all into the Medicare Part D calculator.

Next, we'll choose your pharmacy. We'll look at the pharmacy or pharmacies you prefer. This decision is based entirely on your preference. Some pharmacies may cover your medications better than others, but ultimately, it's your choice.

Then, we'll compare all the available prescription drug plans in your area. In some areas, there are about 15 or 16 different plans—sometimes more—so there are plenty of options. But here's what I always say: the computer will identify the best plan for us.

This makes the process very straightforward. After we enter your personal information, the system will tell us which plan is best for you. Then, we'll enroll you in that plan.

Pretty simple, right? We'll enter the appropriate information, enroll you in the plan, and then each year, we'll re-evaluate it.

If you remember my discussion about the annual enrollment period (October 15 through December 7), that is our opportunity every year to review and adjust your plan as needed.

OUR PART D PROCESS

1 INPUT	Input drug list into Medicare's online calculator	
2 CHOOSE	Choose your pharmacy	
3 COMPARE	Compare all plan options available in your zip code	
4 ENROLL	Enroll into Plan of your choice	
5 RE-EVALUATE	Re-evaluate each Annual Election Period (Oct. 15th - Dec. 7th)	

Figure 4.2

And more often than not, that's exactly what happens. Your health changes every year. Your medications change every year. That's why the annual review and re-evaluation process is so important. We have to make sure your plan keeps up with your personal changes. Just because a Prescription Drug plan works for you one year doesn't mean it will be the best plan for you the next year.

This is often the hardest concept for clients to grasp: Medicare is not a set-it-and-forget-it decision. Top-level service and expertise mean re-evaluating your plan each year to ensure you're on the right Part D prescription plan—not just for this year, but for the years and decades ahead. So whether you're working with us or someone else, make sure they are reviewing your prescription plan annually.

I also want to highlight the Inflation Reduction Act. If you've been on Medicare before 2025, you know that prescription drug plans used to work differently. There was the donut hole, along with various coverage stages. But in 2025, all of that went away. The system is now much simpler to understand.

Now, there is a $2,000 annual cap on prescription drug costs. This is a huge improvement for people who take multiple medications. If you require several prescriptions, this change benefits you significantly. Before this change, there was no cap—you would continue paying co-insurance indefinitely, regardless of how much you had already spent on medications. This new $2,000 cap means you will never spend more than that amount out-of-pocket on your prescriptions in a single year.

This is a very good thing for someone taking a lot of prescriptions, including cancer medications, heart and stroke medications, rheuma-toid arthritis medications, and insulin. It's a very beneficial change.

However, for this savings or cap to exist, the money has to be accounted for elsewhere. What has happened as a result is an increase in deductibles and an increase in plan premiums. For people who do not take medications, this may have affected them negatively. Overall, the impact of the Inflation Reduction Act means there will be fewer plans to choose from. Each of those plans must now include a $2,000 maximum out-of-pocket cap, as long as your prescriptions are in formulary. The key phrase here is "in formulary."

Bringing umbrella coverage back into focus—and as you may see in the next chart—we always recommend umbrella coverage, especially for prescription coverage. A major gap that umbrella coverage helps fill is the cost of prescriptions.

UMBRELLA COVERAGE OPTIONS
*Eliminates **Major** Exposures*

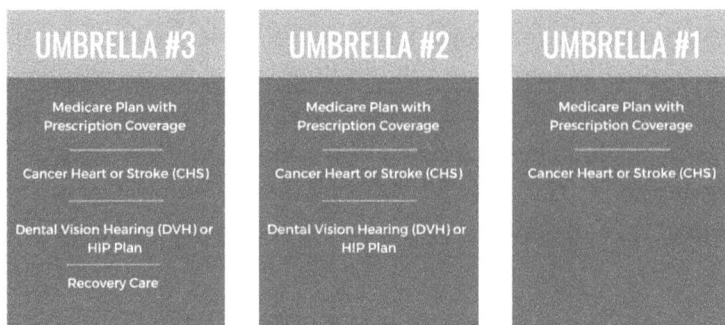

UMBRELLA #3	UMBRELLA #2	UMBRELLA #1
Medicare Plan with Prescription Coverage	Medicare Plan with Prescription Coverage	Medicare Plan with Prescription Coverage
Cancer Heart or Stroke (CHS)	Cancer Heart or Stroke (CHS)	Cancer Heart or Stroke (CHS)
Dental Vision Hearing (DVH) or HIP Plan	Dental Vision Hearing (DVH) or HIP Plan	
Recovery Care		

Figure 4.3

The cancer, heart attack, and stroke coverage included in umbrella coverage protects you from non-formulary prescription costs. It also helps bridge the gap in max out-of-pocket expenses.

To wrap up this section, no matter which Prescription Drug plan you choose, it is crucial to have umbrella coverage. This will help cover any gaps in prescription drug costs that you may be responsible for. At the end of the day, this is part of our service and process. We will input your prescriptions, find the best plan for you, and make everything as simple as possible.

This is a highly individualized conversation. Some people may have a very quick and simple process, while others may require more time and planning. That's why I don't want to take up too much of this book going into every possible scenario.

We touched on this briefly with Larry's story. Larry, as you may recall, chose not to have prescription coverage during his first few years on Medicare. As a result, Larry incurred what's called a late enrollment penalty. A late enrollment penalty applies only if you choose not to have prescription coverage when you're first eligible and later decide to enroll in a plan. If you go your entire life without prescription drug coverage, you will not have a penalty. It only applies if you go without coverage and then decide to enroll at a later date.

People often ask me, "What is the late enrollment penalty?" The penalty is calculated based on the number of uncovered months you went without a Prescription Drug plan before enrolling. It varies for each person. The national average late enrollment penalty is about 33 cents per uncovered month. For example, if someone went without a Prescription Drug plan for five years, we could calculate an estimated penalty. However, it is unique to each person's situation.

Long story short, there are some very inexpensive prescription drug plans available. If you are concerned about the penalty, I urge you to enroll in a plan—even if you are not currently taking any medications. If you choose not to, just be aware that you could face a penalty later if you decide to enroll in a plan.

As we wrap up this chapter, I want to reiterate that prescription drug coverage is a highly individualized decision. For example, my own mother-in-law, Lynnie, takes far more prescriptions than my father-in-law, Mike. She also has some serious health conditions, as I mentioned earlier, including a seizure disorder. She has been on Medicare disability since her early 50s, so her list of prescriptions is naturally more extensive than my father-in-law's. They are, therefore, on completely different prescription plans, and that's okay. That's exactly how it should be if you're working with the right person.

We evaluate spouses individually. We evaluate every person individually. When you take an individualized approach, you ensure that each person gets the right plan for their specific needs. That's what everyone reading this book needs to understand—prescription drug plans are highly personalized. They are tailored to your specific medications.

Our goal is to make sure you have the right price, the right plan, and the right coverage for your unique situation.

CHAPTER 5
MEDICARE ADVANTAGE DEEP DIVE

As we start Chapter 5, we're going to take a deep dive into Medicare Advantage.

If you remember from earlier in the book, we briefly reviewed the differences between Medicare Supplement and Medicare Advantage. Medicare Supplement plans cost more, but they provide more comprehensive coverage and leave you with less financial exposure. With a Medicare Supplement, you can see any provider you want.

Medicare Advantage plans, on the other hand, typically cost less but leave you with a bit more financial responsibility. They require you to use certain doctors and hospitals to get the best possible price and coverage. However, they also offer additional benefits.

I want to share a couple of stories about clients who have had Medicare Advantage plans over the years and their experiences. And in full transparency, we have thousands of clients on both types of plans. What I really want you to understand as the reader is that Medicare is not a one-size-fits-all decision.

For many people, a Medicare Advantage plan is the right choice. And I'm going to start with a story about Bill, a longtime client of mine.

I still remember knocking on his door years ago. I haven't knocked on doors in about five years, but I remember meeting Bill for the first time. He has always been an extremely friendly guy. One thing I remember about Bill is that he doesn't have a lot of teeth—just being honest—and he always jokes about it. Every time he comes to my office, he brings it up. He's very open about it, and I love chatting with him because he's a super positive guy. He has always had a glass-half-full attitude, and I've had the pleasure of sitting at his kitchen table for years. Since we opened our office a few years ago, he's been visiting regularly, and I always enjoy meeting with him.

Bill originally had a Medicare Supplement plan. He's a great example of someone who transitioned from a Medicare Supplement to a Medicare Advantage plan. The main reason he made the switch was price.

A Medicare Advantage plan costs significantly less. Bill only had one medication, was very healthy, and with the Medicare Advantage plan, he also got dental coverage at no extra cost. His plan included $3,000 a year in dental coverage, and it didn't cost him a dime. Bill took advantage of this benefit and got himself some dentures—so now, he has a much better smile. He was always smiling before, but let's be honest—smiling with one or two teeth versus smiling with dentures is a completely different experience. I'm really happy for Bill that we were able to help him get the smile he deserves at no cost to him.

In addition to dental coverage, his plan includes vision and hearing benefits. And most importantly, it fits within his budget. Bill is someone who has to be mindful of his expenses and live more paycheck to paycheck.

Everyone's situation is different, and that's why these plans need to be tailored to each person. For Bill, this was the best fit. He has a good health history, and he doesn't use the plan frequently. When you do the math, over the past three or four years, Bill has saved thousands of dollars in premium costs by switching plans.

And if he ever faces a serious illness, he has umbrella coverage with his Medicare Advantage plan. This ensures that in the event of a catastrophic event—such as a hospital stay, cancer, heart attack, or stroke—he is well taken care of. It's always great to see Bill each year and know that we adjusted his coverage based on his unique needs.

That's a really great story about Bill. Now, for story number two, let's go back to Larry from earlier in the book. Larry is a wealthy client who has a Medicare Advantage plan. Whether you are wealthy or living on a fixed income, a Medicare Advantage plan can work for both situations. Larry, as you may recall, initially went without coverage because, as a wealthy individual, he believed he didn't need it. He said, "I don't need it. I don't want it."

Then, he was diagnosed with leukemia. At that point, the only option left for him was a Medicare Advantage plan. But he couldn't even enroll in one until the open enrollment period. That meant he went six months without a plan, leaving him responsible for 20% of his medical costs. Remember, Medicare Part B requires you to pay 20% of medical expenses—with no cap. For those six months, Larry was responsible for 20% of all his procedures, medications, and treatments, with no limit to how much he could owe. Now that he has a Medicare Advantage plan, it doesn't cost him anything extra—but it does provide one major benefit: it sets a cap on his out-of-pocket expenses. So now, he has a plan with a built-in limit. Once he reaches that limit for the year, he no longer has to pay for covered expenses out-of-pocket.

Larry is someone I really enjoy talking to. We have great conversations, and he is an incredibly intelligent guy. And for his situation, a Medicare Advantage plan was the only viable option at that point. But even then, it was still a much better option than having no plan at all.

That's the key takeaway from Larry's story: if you don't want to pay extra for coverage, whether you're rich, poor, or somewhere in between, a Medicare Advantage plan provides additional coverage at no extra cost. That's why it's so important to carefully evaluate these plans and understand their benefits. Having worked with thousands of people on Medicare Advantage plans, I've seen them in action during both the best and worst times in people's lives. And I can tell you—they work in both situations.

With those two stories to establish the context, let's now get into the details—the educational side of Medicare Advantage plans. To provide a short summary, Medicare Advantage plans are managed care plans. You are still responsible for paying your Medicare Part B premium. However, the key difference is that when you enroll in a Medicare Advantage plan, you are leaving the federal Medicare system and moving to a private insurance company that manages your care. For example, many major companies offer Medicare Advantage plans. What happens here is that instead of Medicare handling your benefits directly, the federal government pays these private insurance companies a monthly stipend to manage your care.

OPTION 2: MEDICARE ADVANTAGE PLANS

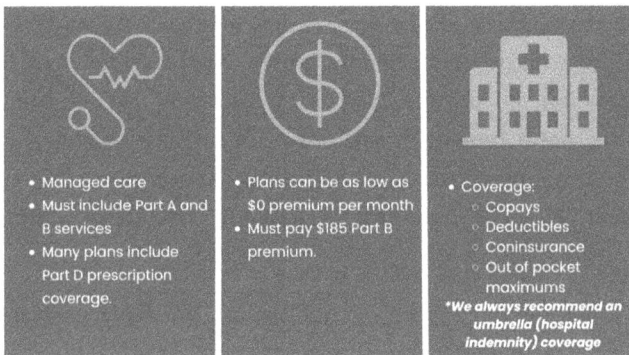

- Managed care
- Must include Part A and B services
- Many plans include Part D prescription coverage.

- Plans can be as low as $0 premium per month
- Must pay $185 Part B premium.

- Coverage:
  ○ Copays
  ○ Deductibles
  ○ Coinsurance
  ○ Out of pocket maximums
  We always recommend an umbrella (hospital indemnity) coverage

Figure 5.1

These companies have a lot of skin in the game. They want you to be healthy. They want to manage their care—your care. They want you to have as few claims as possible so they remain profitable. Because of this, there is a benefit to managed care. These companies have a vested interest in ensuring their private insurance plans remain successful.

To encourage this, they offer many extra benefits. They entice you with incentives and encourage you to visit the doctor regularly, ensuring that you are proactive with your health rather than reactive.

So there are definite advantages to Medicare Advantage plans. But remember, when you enroll in one, you are moving into private healthcare and managed care. However, the one key rule is that these plans must provide you with the same basic benefits as Original Medicare (Parts A and B). That means they must still cover the same 20% Part B co-insurance and hospital exposure that Original Medicare covers.

The difference is that, with a Medicare Advantage plan, that 20% and the hospital co-insurance gaps are your responsibility. There are ways to reduce this exposure—such as using umbrella coverage to make it function more like a Medicare Supplement—but it's important to understand that these plans can vary significantly.

In this chapter, you won't find a graph showing exact plans because, again, Medicare Advantage plans are based on your zip code. They differ substantially from state to state. For example, plans available in California may look completely different from those in Maine. That's why it's essential to evaluate plans based on your zip code and county to understand exactly what is available to you.

These plans can be as low as zero premium. You've probably seen the advertisements—zero-premium plans, food cards, and all sorts of extra benefits being promoted when you turn 65. However, one thing to keep in mind with these plans is that they include co-pays, deductibles, co-insurance, and out-of-pocket maximums.

With a Medicare Supplement, most of this exposure is covered. With a Medicare Advantage plan, you pay less upfront but take on more financial responsibility. For this reason, we never recommend a Medicare Advantage plan without umbrella coverage. Very rarely do we see someone enroll in a Medicare Advantage plan without some form of umbrella coverage.

So how do you choose a Medicare Advantage plan?

First and foremost, your zip code matters. But beyond that, the most critical factors are your doctors, hospitals, and medications. Every plan has a formulary. And we have to look and see if your medications are in that plan.

CHOOSING A MEDICARE ADVANTAGE PLAN

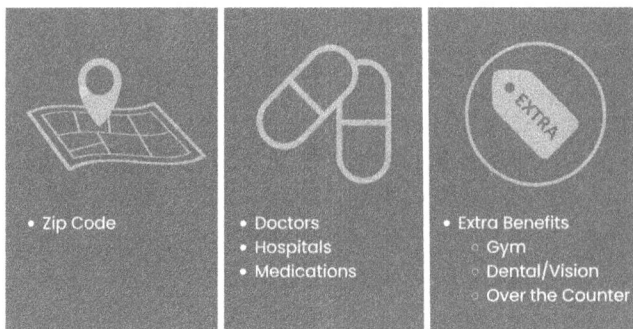

| • Zip Code | • Doctors
• Hospitals
• Medications | • Extra Benefits
○ Gym
○ Dental/Vision
○ Over the Counter |

Figure 5.2

The first thing I look for is whether your medications are covered by the plan. Next, I check if your doctors are in-network. If your doctors are included, hospitals usually are as well, but we verify hospital coverage too. The key deciding factors for these plans are doctors, hospitals, and medications—along with the extra benefits they offer.

For example, one of my clients wanted dental coverage. This plan provided free dental. Almost all of these plans also include a free gym membership.

These companies want you to stay healthy. They want to manage your care proactively so you live longer, which is why they offer free gym memberships.

Many plans also include vision and hearing benefits, as well as over-the-counter allowances. If you qualify, some even provide food cards or spending card benefits. These plans come with a variety of additional perks designed to enhance your overall healthcare experience.

One thing we always do is pull up the outline of coverage for these plans. The outline of coverage allows you to see exactly what your benefits look like—how much you pay for a procedure, how much you pay for a hospital stay, and how much you pay for a doctor visit. It provides a clear breakdown of your coverage.

Then, we take that umbrella coverage and layer it on top to help fill in the gaps.

To help you shop for Medicare Advantage plans on your own, SCAN THE QR CODE:

Simply type in your zip code, search for Medicare Advantage plans, and see what is available in your area.

The next question I often get is, "Chase, how and when do I sign up for these plans?"

These plans work slightly differently. You have to wait until at least three months before you turn 65 to sign up for a Medicare Advantage plan.

HOW AND WHEN TO SIGN UP

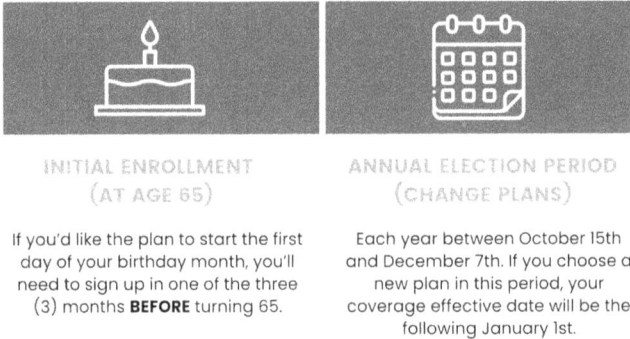

INITIAL ENROLLMENT (AT AGE 65)	ANNUAL ELECTION PERIOD (CHANGE PLANS)
If you'd like the plan to start the first day of your birthday month, you'll need to sign up in one of the three (3) months **BEFORE** turning 65.	Each year between October 15th and December 7th. If you choose a new plan in this period, your coverage effective date will be the following January 1st.

Figure 5.4

In comparison, Medicare Supplement enrollment can begin six months before you turn 65, whereas Medicare Advantage enrollment starts three months prior.

Each year, there is also an annual enrollment period from October 15 through December 7. This is when you can make changes to your Medicare Advantage plan. Additionally, there is a Medicare Advantage open enrollment period from January through March, during which you can make a one-time change.

These plans have more restrictions on when you can change them, which is why using a broker is so valuable—especially when dealing with Medicare Advantage plans. Having a trusted representative or educator is crucial because Medicare Advantage plans can be complex. I see many people make poor decisions when choosing these plans, and I cannot emphasize enough—if you are considering Medicare Advantage, do not navigate this alone.

There are many different plan types, including PPOs, HMOs, and POS plans. If you don't know what those mean, that's another reason to work with a broker or educator.

These acronyms refer to network types:

- **PPO (Preferred Provider Organization)** allows more flexibility in choosing doctors and hospitals.
- **HMO (Health Maintenance Organization)** has a more restrictive network with required referrals.
- **POS (Point of Service)** combines elements of both, sometimes allowing out-of-network care at a higher cost.

It is important to understand these differences before enrolling in a plan.

As we wrap up our discussion of these two options, we are moving through the core of this book. We've covered Medicare Supplement plans, prescription drug coverage, and Medicare Advantage plans. I don't want to overcomplicate this book, so if you had to take away one key comparison, this is it:

- **Medicare Supplements**: You pay more, but you have more comprehensive coverage and less financial exposure.
- **Medicare Advantage:** You pay less upfront, but you take on more financial exposure.

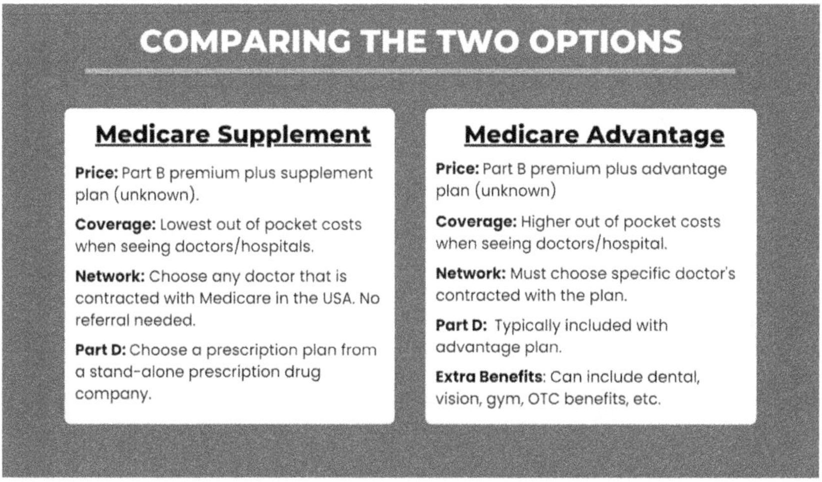

COMPARING THE TWO OPTIONS

Medicare Supplement

Price: Part B premium plus supplement plan (unknown).

Coverage: Lowest out of pocket costs when seeing doctors/hospitals.

Network: Choose any doctor that is contracted with Medicare in the USA. No referral needed.

Part D: Choose a prescription plan from a stand-alone prescription drug company.

Medicare Advantage

Price: Part B premium plus advantage plan (unknown)

Coverage: Higher out of pocket costs when seeing doctors/hospital.

Network: Must choose specific doctor's contracted with the plan.

Part D: Typically included with advantage plan.

Extra Benefits: Can include dental, vision, gym, OTC benefits, etc.

Figure 5.5

These plans often come with additional benefits, which may be important to you.

And once again, I cannot emphasize enough—whether you choose a Medicare Supplement or a Medicare Advantage plan, do not enroll without umbrella coverage. Umbrella coverage eliminates major catastrophic financial risks and helps protect the assets you've worked so hard to accumulate. It ensures your legacy remains intact and prevents your savings from being drained by costly medical events like cancer treatment or nursing home care.

As we wrap up this chapter, I want to reiterate that these plans offer significant value and are the right fit for many people. That's why, during our one-on-one call, our job is to understand you as an individual, assess your needs, and determine the plan, price, and coverage that best suit your unique situation.

CHAPTER 6
RETIREMENT PLANNING

A lot of people come to us—almost everyone—for Medicare planning, and that's really what we market: Medicare. But if you've seen our tagline, you know it's Medicare and retirement planning. It's what we do. Gruening Health and Wealth is our main consumer brand, and a lot of people ask, "What do you do on the wealth side?" Over the years, we've seen that people come to us as they enter their retirement years—their golden years—at 64, 65, and beyond. Most are transitioning from their working life.

With this transition to Medicare, we also started seeing a major financial transition. That made me stop and think: we need to offer more. We need to provide a more holistic approach to Medicare and retirement planning. That's exactly what we did—we launched a retirement division in 2016, which I now lead.

I focus on guiding people through the transition from their working years to their non-working years, when they move from earning and investing to drawing from their savings and no longer investing the way they used to. One thing I always caution people about is how drastically their financial situation changes in retirement. Think about it: for the past 30 years, you've likely been investing aggressively, keeping your money in higher-risk accounts. But now, you're no longer earning income as you're no longer working, yet many people make no financial changes. That is the biggest mistake I see—people either continue doing exactly what they've done for decades or they do nothing at all. That's what I urge you to think about right now: have you taken a step back and evaluated your financial transition? Are you still following the same financial strategy you used for the last 30 years, even though your life has completely changed? To wrap this up, I highly recommend taking a close look at your financial picture and retirement planning.

With all of these changes, have you adjusted your financial strategy accordingly? Have you ensured that your retirement plan aligns with your new reality? At the very least, have you taken the time to assess what's actually happening with your financial future? We'll discuss what can happen if you don't in just a moment. But first, I want to share a quick story about a client of mine who, unfortunately, passed away this past year.

He had a portfolio worth over a million dollars, which we had the opportunity to service and protect. He was an interesting case—he had been with us for six or seven years, but it took five or six years before he decided to become one of our financial clients. Our primary focus is protection and growth. We help eliminate downside risk while still capturing upside growth—without any risk to principal protection. Long story short, he eventually moved his million-dollar portfolio to our practice. Within 18 months, we were able to grow his account by 30% while ensuring that his principal remained protected. Because of this, his legacy has now been passed on to his two sons, without any financial risk at all.

If he had left his money where it was, this would not have been the case. His beneficiaries would have missed out on that 30% growth, his portfolio would have been exposed to significant downside risk, and the process of transferring his assets would have been far more compli-cated. Instead, we were able to protect his portfolio from downside risk, grow it by 30%, and pass his wealth on to his beneficiaries smoothly and without issue. Within 30 days, his sons were able to access his account and secure his legacy—exactly as he intended.

So, that's a story I look back on, one that I'm really proud of, and that's what we do for all of our clients. We're able to protect that legacy, grow that legacy, and ultimately make sure that legacy lives on far beyond them.

What I really want to teach you—the reader—is the types of accounts that we deal with mainly. There are really three pillars that we focus on. The first one is safe money retirement. Going back to the beginning of this chapter, I mentioned that when so much has changed, it would be absolutely insane to keep doing the same thing. I want you to think about this, and it's something I always talk to our clients about using a simple example. Let's say you have a million-dollar portfolio. If you're 65 years old and that portfolio increases by 10%, bringing your total to $1.1 million, it's probably not going to impact your life significantly, and most clients would agree with me.

Going from $1 million to $1.1 million is not going to change your life much. Now, on the opposite end of that spectrum, if your $1 million portfolio drops to $900,000 or even $800,000 due to a 10% to 20% market downturn, that will absolutely impact your life. Almost everyone agrees that if their account goes down 10% or 20%, it will greatly affect their future. The biggest issue here is that, in this scenario, you are no longer working, which means you are no longer contributing to these accounts.

In the past, during recessionary periods, market downturns didn't worry most people because they were still working and actively contributing to their accounts. If their balance dropped, they could continue investing, and over time, their accounts would recover—often growing even more in the long run. However, once you're retired, if your account value drops and you need to withdraw funds without replenishing them, you start to run out of money. That's the biggest issue I see with our clients—they keep their money in high-risk assets or portfolios despite no longer contributing.

And that's exactly what we advise taking a look at here—how to protect that principal, continue to grow it, and eliminate any downside risk. So we focus on safe money retirement, where we protect your money while still allowing it to grow. We deal with all types of accounts—401(k)s, IRAs, 403(b)s, 457s, brokerage accounts, money markets, CDs, and cash.

SAFE MONEY RETIREMENT

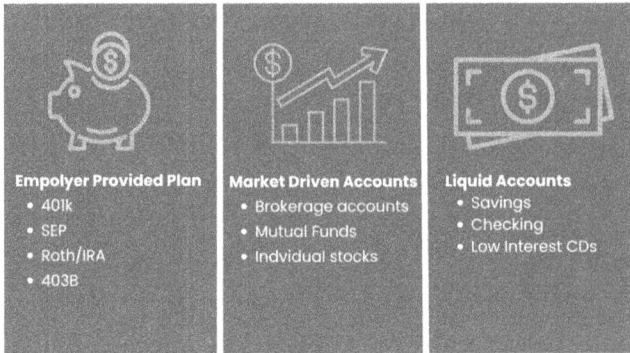

Figure 6.1

I have seen absolutely everything. It doesn't matter what type of retirement account you have; we have worked with those types of accounts, found homes for them, and understand what you're going through with them.

Now, as I mentioned, one of our main pillars is safe money retirement. The second is growth. How do we accomplish this growth? We use guaranteed fixed index rates and index growth, which allow for much higher potential long-term growth. Everything we do is tax-deferred, helping your money grow more efficiently while avoiding probate and ensuring that your legacy is protected. We have income products available that can create pension-like income for you, growth products designed to maximize your investments, and legacy products to ensure your wealth is passed on efficiently and securely.

SAFE MONEY RETIREMENT

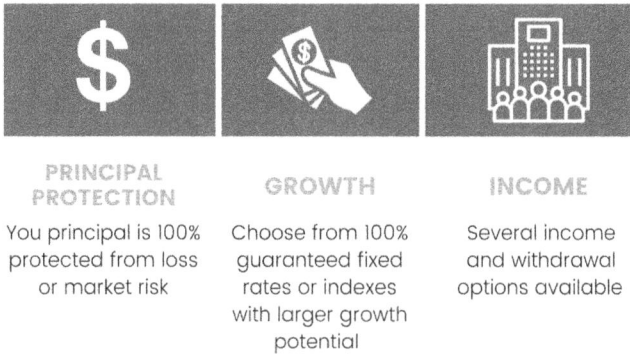

PRINCIPAL PROTECTION	GROWTH	INCOME
You principal is 100% protected from loss or market risk	Choose from 100% guaranteed fixed rates or indexes with larger growth potential	Several income and withdrawal options available

Figure 6.2

So, the main thing I do when I sit down with a client is walk them through a short discovery call. And during this call, I do very little talking. All I want to know is, what are you trying to accomplish? What are we trying to solve? What is the goal here? Are you trying to pass money along? Are you trying to create an income stream? Are you trying to grow your accounts? What I really want to know is: *What is most important to you?*

That is always my goal when it comes to retirement planning—to understand your unique financial picture and determine how we can enhance it. And that's really what it all comes down to. Our approach is simple.

I handle the entire retirement planning process for you. We put together your budget, assess your assets and liabilities, and develop a plan tailored specifically to you. This is a full-service approach where we'll be there year after year, helping you make important decisions and guiding you every step of the way.

One of the key benefits of working with us is that we have no fees. Most brokerage firms or financial advisors charge a half percent to a full percent in fees. We do not. We simply broker these products and are compensated by the companies themselves. This allows us to protect our clients' legacies while ensuring a smooth financial transition.

That word *transition* is something I always emphasize. Many people don't realize that as they go through this critical phase in life, they also need to consider their financial transition.

I'll wrap this up by saying that what I can hang my hat on at night is knowing that our clients' money has always been protected, even during major financial crises. We've been through the 2008 recession, COVID, and other volatile periods. In times of uncertainty, our clients have had stability.

That's what I'm most proud of: when a client calls me after seeing the market drop 30%–40% in a matter of weeks, like it did during COVID, and they're relieved because their money was secure. Number one, they don't have time to recover from massive losses at this stage in life. Number two, we provided them with peace of mind when there was very little of it in the world.

So, if you have retirement questions, that's an appointment you'll have directly with me. It starts with a simple discovery call, where we'll walk through your financial transition, explore your options, and help you gain a clearer understanding of what your future looks like.

Let's dive a little deeper into the types of retirement accounts you may have and that we frequently work with. The most common retirement accounts are those offered through an employer, including 401(k)s, 457s, and 403(b)s. These accounts are typically funded through contributions from both you and your employer during your working years. Often, they are associated with active management fees and invested in a combination of mutual funds and bonds, which can make them volatile. As a general rule, many people choose to roll these accounts over into an IRA or move them out of their employer's plan upon retirement.

The reason for this is that many of these accounts, as I alluded to earlier, have fees associated with them. Moving them away from an employer, where policies and management can often change—especially once you've separated—has become a common rule of thumb.

The second type of retirement accounts we frequently see are IRAs, or Roth accounts that you may have contributed to over the years. Depending on how those accounts have been invested—whether self-managed or managed by an advisor—they may now be higher-risk accounts that you are no longer contributing to or have significantly slowed down contributions to. These are tax-deferred accounts or accounts with different tax implications, which is something we can evaluate as well.

Another area I see frequently is liquid assets. This includes cash sitting in the bank at a very low interest rate, cash kept under the mattress or in a safe, or CDs with minimal interest earnings. These are short-term solutions, as we call them, but many people who have money allocated in short-term solutions are actually looking for a long-term plan. Liquid assets like cash or CDs tend to be the lowest-performing assets in a portfolio, and when viewed from a long-term perspective, they can actually cause financial loss due to inflation.

No matter which type of account you have—whether it carries risk or is low-risk—we are able to structure these accounts in ways that provide significant value in terms of growth, protection, tax deferral, and income streams. I know you, as the reader, may be asking, what types of accounts do you work with? The answer is that many of the accounts we deal with share the same fundamental structure.

As I mentioned earlier, they all have principal protection, meaning they cannot lose value—there is no possibility of negative interest. All of these accounts also have indexed or fixed growth potential, which means they come with a guaranteed rate of return, often in the range of 4% to 5%. In many cases, we aim for something even stronger, so we incorporate indexed growth, which allows returns to be tied to market performance while still providing downside protection. This means that while the accounts have higher growth potential, they still cannot lose value. For example, we have seen clients achieve returns of 13% to 14% with absolutely no risk.

Lastly, all of our products offer tax-deferred growth, meaning you don't pay taxes on earnings until you withdraw the money. They also avoid probate, ensuring a smooth transfer of assets. Additionally, we have the ability to design these products to create income streams, whether in the form of guaranteed lifetime income—similar to a pension—or flexible withdrawals as needed, with liquidity available to you.

Put simply, we work with all types of retirement accounts and financial situations. More importantly, we help provide protection, growth, safety, and—above all—peace of mind over time.

CONCLUSION
PUTTING IT ALL TOGETHER

F irst of all, I want to thank you, the reader, for making it through this book. This is your guide to Medicare and retirement planning, and in my opinion, it is the resource you need to get started on your journey.

We have what we call a three-phased approach. The first phase is Medicare education, and you can almost check that off your list. My only other recommendation is to watch the video linked through the QR code at the beginning of the book.

Since you've read the book, the next step is to watch the video, where you'll get to see me face-to-face. I'll be teaching you in video format exactly what we just covered in this book. In my opinion, the combination of this book and the video will provide all the knowledge you need to make the right decisions. We've helped thousands and thousands of Medicare beneficiaries just like you through our in-person, online, and book education programs. This process has empowered them to make the right decisions with confidence and clarity as they enter the complex world of Medicare—or, if they were already on Medicare, to make better decisions about their current plan.

Again, we support people whether they are enrolling in Medicare for the first time or have been on Medicare for years. Our goal is to ensure they are maximizing their coverage and making the best choices available to them.

I want to share a quick story. Over the years, we've helped countless people one-on-one, whether in person, over the phone, or via video. One client who comes to mind is Shirley, who has been with me ever since I started almost eight or nine years ago. Every year, she comes into my office, sits down, and tells me how thankful she is for our help. Before I had an office, I visited her at home and sat with her on her couch. She was overpaying for her plans and had no idea what she was doing. We were able to save her a significant amount of money. Since then, we haven't had to make many changes—just monitoring her plans to ensure she isn't paying more than she should. But for her, simply having someone she trusts and can turn to for guidance is invaluable.

I recently read a statistic: there are 61.2 million Medicare beneficiaries in the country, but only about 100,000 Medicare agents available to help them. In my opinion, only a small percentage of those agents are truly helpful. Medicare is an underserved market, and when I see people like Shirley—who we've been able to help for years, whether in person, over the phone, or via video—it reaffirms just how much people need and appreciate this guidance. I look forward to working with Shirley every year, and she even brings me a little Christmas gift now. It's been enjoyable to get to know her.

Phase two of our process is enrollment advice, which includes a free consultation. We provide the book, the video, various online resources, and our YouTube channel to make sure you are well informed and prepared.

Even if you don't have additional questions, you will need to check this off your list. Phase two ensures that you receive personalized enrollment advice.

Schedule your one-on-one call, where you'll meet with one of our agents whom I have personally trained. Whether you speak with me or one of my colleagues, we will walk you through everything you need to know to make the best decisions for yourself. We'll also answer any questions that are unique to your situation.

I know there are many different readers going through this book, each with their own unique questions—what about this, what about that, or my situation is this, my situation is that. Those are the questions we need to get answered. We want to make sure you walk away with clarity, having checked everything off your list.

So be sure to take advantage of the free enrollment advice. There is absolutely no cost for any of our services, as we mentioned earlier. Then, in phase three, you'll receive lifetime service and support, and that is what I am most proud of.

We have a fantastic administrative staff dedicated to handling everything for you. Our internal team will ensure that every detail is taken care of. You'll have an annual review each year to make sure your plans are still the right fit, and you'll have access to an outstanding customer service team providing lifetime billing and claims support. You will never have to call an insurance company or speak with anyone other than our team—we will handle absolutely everything related to your Medicare and retirement planning.

That's what I'm most proud of: we have built a nationwide practice focused entirely on serving Medicare beneficiaries and retirees across the country. I truly hope you'll be the next person we have the privilege of helping.

I can't say it enough—thank you so much for taking the time to read this book. We all have limited time, and I sincerely appreciate that you chose to spend yours here. Whether it took you 60 minutes, 90 minutes, or you read this over the course of a few days or weeks, I truly appreciate it.

I want to personally thank you for reading, and I hope to see you or hear from you during an upcoming consultation. If not, I would love it if you could leave us a five-star review on our website and let us know you enjoyed the book. Thank you so much, wishing you all the best, and we'll talk to you soon.

THANK YOU FOR READING MY BOOK!

Book your Free Medicare Planning Call

As a thank-you for reading *64+*, I'd love to offer you a **complimentary
call** with our team. We'll help you understand your Medicare options
and answer any questions you may have.
Scan the QR code to schedule your call.
We're here to make Medicare easier — one step at a time.

*I appreciate your interest in my book and value your feedback as it helps
me improve future versions of this book.
I would appreciate it if you could leave your invaluable review on
Amazon.com with your feedback.
Thank you!*